REVISE FOR Edexcel GCSE MATHEMATICS

HIGHER

Keith Pledger David Kent

About this book

This book is designed to help you get your best possible grade in your Edexcel GCSE Mathematics examination. The authors are the Chair of Examiners and the Subject Officer for Mathematics, and have a good understanding of Edexcel's requirements.

Revise for Edexcel GCSE: Higher covers key topics that are often tested in the Higher level exam papers, focusing mainly on grades A*, A and B. *Revise for Edexcel GCSE Mathematics: Intermediate* focuses mainly on grades B, C and D, whilst *Revise for Edexcel GCSE Mathematics: Foundation* is focused on Grades D, E and F.

You can use the book to help you revise at the end of your course, or you can use it throughout your course alongside the course textbook: *Edexcel GCSE Mathematics: Higher* which provides complete coverage of the syllabus.

Helping you prepare for your exam

To help you prepare, each topic offers you:

Key points to remember – These summarize the mathematical ideas you need to know and be able to use.

Worked examples and examination questions – help you understand and remember important methods, and show you how to set out your answers clearly.

Revision exercises – help you practice using important methods to solve problems. Past paper questions are included so you can be sure you are reaching the right standard, and answers are given at the back of the book so you can assess your progress.

Test yourself questions – help you see where you need extra revision and practice. If you do need extra help they show you where to look in the *Edexcel GCSE Mathematics: Higher* textbook.

Exam practice and advice on revising

Examination style practice paper – this paper at the end of the book provides a set of questions of examination standard. It gives you an opportunity to practice taking a complete exam before you meet the real thing.

How to revise – For advice on revising before the exam, read the **How to revise** section on the next two pages.

How to revise using this book

Making the best use of your revision time

The topics in this book have been arranged in a logical sequence so you can work your way through them from beginning to end. But **how** you work on them depends on how much time there is between now and your examination.

If you have plenty of time before the exam (at least 8 weeks) then you can **work through each topic in turn**, covering the key points and worked examples before doing the revision exercises and test yourself questions.

If you are short of time then you can **work through the Test yourself sections first** to help you see which topics you need to do further work on.

However much time you have to revise in, make sure you break your revision into short blocks of about 40 minutes, separated by five or ten minute breaks. Nobody can study effectively for hours without a break.

Using the Test yourself sections

Each test yourself section provides a set of key questions. Try each question:

If you can do it and get the correct answer then move on to the next topic. Come back to this topic later to consolidate your knowledge and understanding by working through the key points, worked examples and revision exercises.

If you cannot do the question, or get an incorrect answer or part answer then work through the key points, worked examples and revision exercises before trying the test yourself questions again. If you need more help, the cross-references beside each test yourself question show you where to find relevant information in the *Edexcel GCSE Mathematics: Higher* textbook.

Reviewing the key points

Most of the key points are straightforward ideas that you can learn: try to understand each one. Imagine explaining each idea to a friend in your own words, and say it out loud as you do so. This is a better way of making the ideas stick than just reading them silently from the page.

As you work through the book, remember to go back over key points from earlier topics at least once a week. This will help you to remember them in the exam.

Working on the worked examples

Read each question at the start of each worked example and think about what it is asking you to do. Try to work out which key point(s) you need to use, and how to answer the question before you look at the answer itself.

The answer will tell you which key point(s) to use. Read this again if you need to.

Follow the working through carefully, making sure you understand each stage. The notes in the margin give useful information – make sure you read them.

Using the revision exercises

Tackle the revision exercises in the same way as the worked examples. If you need to, go back to the key points and worked examples to see which method to use.

If you are not sure what to do, look at the answer at the back of the book to see if this gives you a clue. (For example – units such as £, or a % sign will give you a hint.)

Try to set out your answers in a similar way to the worked examples, showing all the stages in your working. In an examination you can gain marks by doing this. If the examiner understands that you have the right method you may gain some marks even if you make an error in a calculation.

Taking the practice exam

The Higher GSCE papers are one and a half hours long, so put aside one and a half hours when you know you will not be disturbed and try to do the practice exam all in one go. This will give you some idea of how you need to pace yourself when you do the real thing.

Usually the easier topics come first in the exam, so most people start at the beginning to gain confidence by answering questions successfully.

Also, you may have some favourite topics you want to get under your belt first, so look through the whole paper at the start to get a feel for all the questions to be covered.

Wherever you start, **read the questions carefully**. Many candidates lose marks because they haven't done this.

As for the revision exercises, show all the stages in your working. If a question has 4 marks then 1 or 2 of them will be for the answer and the rest for the method you have used.

After finishing the practice exam, check your answers. If an answer is incorrect, check through your method making sure you haven't made any errors in your working.

If you can't find your mistake, use the cross reference by each question as a guide to see what to review. If you still can't find your mistake, ask your teacher to help you.

1 Simplifying algebraic expressions

Key points to remember

1 $x^m \times x^n = x^{m+n}$
For example, $3y^2 \times 2y^3 = 6y^{2+3} = 6y^5$

Remember x is the *base* and n is the *index* or power (plural indices)

2 $(x^m)^n = x^{mn}$
For example, $(x^2)^3 = x^{2\times 3} = x^6$

3 $x^m \div x^n = x^{m-n}$
For example, $6^6 \div 6^2 = 6^{6-2} = 6^4$

4 $x^0 = 1$ when $x \neq 0$

5 $x^{-n} = \dfrac{1}{x^n}$

For example, $2^{-3} = \dfrac{1}{2^3} = \dfrac{1}{8}$

6 $x^{\frac{1}{n}} = \sqrt[n]{x}$,
For example, $16^{\frac{1}{2}} = \sqrt{16} = \pm 4$

7 $x^{\frac{m}{n}} = (\sqrt[n]{x})^m$ or $\sqrt[n]{x^m}$
For example, $16^{\frac{5}{4}} = (\sqrt[4]{16})^5 = (2)^5 = 32$

8 $\dfrac{1}{n} + \dfrac{1}{m} = \dfrac{m+n}{mn}$

9 An expression of the form $ax^2 + bx + c$, with $a \neq 0$, is called a quadratic in x.

10 To factorize $ax^2 + bx$ take out the Highest Common Factor.
For example, $4x^2 + 10x = 2x(2x + 5)$

11 To factorize $ax^2 + bx + c$, start by looking for two numbers whose product is ac and whose sum is b.

12 $x^2 - y^2 = (x - y)(x + y)$

13 $x^2 + 2ax + a^2 = (x + a)^2$

14 $x^2 - 2ax + a^2 = (x - a)^2$

Worked examination question 1 [L]

(a) Simplify $x^4 \div x^{-3}$

(b) Find the value of x for which $4^{\frac{x}{2}} = 32$

Answer

(a) Using **3**

$$x^4 \div x^{-3} = x^{4--3} = x^7$$

Remember $- - = +$

(b) Using **7**

$$4^{\frac{x}{2}} = (\sqrt{4})^x = 2^x$$

Now $32 = 2 \times 2 \times 2 \times 2 \times 2 = 2^5$

Then $2^x = 2^5$

So $x = 5$

Worked examination question 2 [L]

Factorize completely $6x^2 + 9x$

Answer

Using **10** $\quad 6x^2 + 9x = 3x(2x + 3)$

Worked examination question 3 [L]

Simplify

$$\frac{1}{x+3} + \frac{1}{x-5}$$

Answer

Using **8** with $n = (x + 3)$ and $m = (x - 5)$

$$\frac{1}{x+3} + \frac{1}{x-5} = \frac{(x-5)+(x+3)}{(x+3)(x-5)} = \frac{2x-2}{(x+3)(x-5)}$$

Using **10**

$$= \frac{2(x-1)}{(x+3)(x-5)}$$

Worked examination question 4 [L]

(a) Factorize $m^2 - n^2$

(b) Rewrite 9991 as the difference of two squares. Hence find the prime factors of 9991.

Answer

(a) Using **12** $\quad m^2 - n^2 = (m + n)(m - n)$

(b) Using **12**

$$9991 = 10\,000 - 9 = 100^2 - 3^2 = (100 + 3)(100 - 3) = 103 \times 97$$

$\therefore$ prime factors are 103 and 97.

Example 1

Factorize:

(a) $x^2 + 5x - 6$ (b) $6x^2 + 5x - 4$

Answer

(a) Using **11** $a = 1, b = 5, c = -6$
Then $ac = -6$, $b = 5$
Two numbers whose product is -6 and sum is 5 are -1 and 6.
Therefore $x^2 + 5x - 6 = (x - 1)(x + 6)$

$-1 \times 6 = -6$
$-1 + 6 = 5$

(b) Using **11** $ac = -24$, $b = 5$
This is best done by trial and error.

Try $(6x - 4)(x + 1)$
$= 6x^2 + 6x - 4x - 4$ ✗ (wrong)

Try $(2x - 1)(3x + 4)$
$= 6x^2 + 8x - 3x - 4$
$= 6x^2 + 5x - 4$ ✓ (right)

Revision exercise 1

1 Write down the value of
(a) $4^{1\frac{1}{2}}$ **(b)** $27^{-\frac{1}{3}}$ [L]

2 $y = 2^{-x}$
(a) Calculate the value of y when $x = 0$
(b) Calculate the value of y when $x = 3$ [L]

3 $x^2 \times x^3 = x^p$
(a) Write down the value of p.
$\sqrt{x} = x^q$
(b) Write down the value of q.
$(x^2 \times x^3) \div \sqrt{x} = x^r$
(c) By expressing r in terms of p and q, or otherwise, find the value of r. [L]

4 **(a)** Factorize completely $10x^2 - 5x$
(b) Calculate the value of y, when $x^{\frac{1}{2}} \div x^{-3} = x^y$ [L]

5 Factorize completely
(a) $6x^2y^2 - 3x^4y^2$ **(b)** $12xy^3 - 8x^4y$ [L]

6 Factorize completely $ax - by - bx + ay$ [L]

7 Simplify
(a) $a^4 \times a^5$ **(b)** $(x^3)^2$ **(c)** $3x^2 \times 4x^3$
(d) $x^9 \div x^5$ **(e)** $6x^5 \div 2x^2$ **(f)** $(\frac{1}{16})^{\frac{1}{2}}$
(g) $8^{\frac{5}{3}}$ **(h)** $(4x^0)^5$ **(i)** $27^{\frac{2}{3}}$

8 Write as a single fraction in its lowest terms

(a) $\frac{1}{x}+\frac{2}{y}$ **(b)** $\frac{4}{3x}+\frac{5}{6x}$ **(c)** $\frac{x-1}{2}+\frac{x+3}{6}$ **(d)** $\frac{1}{x+2}-\frac{4}{x-1}$

9 Factorize

(a) x^2+4x **(b)** $2x^2y-6xy^2$ **(c)** x^2+3x+2
(d) x^2-5x+4 **(e)** x^2+7x-8 **(f)** $x^2+12x+32$
(g) $2x^2+5x+2$ **(h)** $15x^2-4x-3$ **(i)** $8x^2-14x+3$
(j) $2x^4+7x^2-4$ **(k)** x^2+6x+9 **(l)** $x^2-8x+16$

Test yourself

Test yourself	What to review
	If your answer is incorrect:
1 Simplify $2x^5 \times 3x^2$	*Review Higher book Unit 20, page 357, Examples 1 and 2.*
2 Simplify $10x^6 \div 5x^3$	*Review Higher book Unit 20, page 358, Example 4.*
3 Find the value of $(125)^{-\frac{2}{3}}$	*Review Higher book Unit 20, page 360, Example 5 and page 361, Example 6.*
4 Write as a single fraction $\frac{3}{x+2}-\frac{1}{x+1}$	*Review Higher book Unit 20, page 367, Example 14.*
5 Factorize $6x^2+8x$	*Review Higher book Unit 20, page 371.*
6 Factorize x^2-5x+4	*Review Higher book Unit 20, page 371, Example 18.*
7 Factorize $6x^2+11x-10$	*Review Higher book Unit 20, page 372, Examples 19 and 20.*

Answers to Test yourself

1 $6x^7$ **2** $2x^3$ **3** $\frac{1}{25}$ **4** $\frac{2x+1}{(x+2)(x+1)}$ **5** $2x(3x+4)$ **6** $(x-1)(x-4)$ **7** $(3x-2)(2x+5)$

2 Basic number skills

Key points to remember

1 If an amount increases by $x\%$ the new amount is $(100 + x)\%$ of the original amount.

2 If an amount decreases by $x\%$ the new amount is $(100 - x)\%$ of the original amount.

3 $$\text{Percentage change} = \frac{\text{increase or decrease}}{\text{original}} \times 100\%$$

4 Compound interest is interest paid on an amount and on the interest on that amount.

You can use the formula $$A = P\left(1 + \frac{R}{100}\right)^n$$

where P is the principal (amount lent or borrowed)
R is the rate of interest (% p.a.)
n is the number of years of the investment or loan
A is the amount (principal + compound interest) after n years

5 $$\text{Average speed} = \frac{\text{distance travelled}}{\text{time taken}}$$ (typical units: km/h)

6 $$\text{Density} = \frac{\text{mass}}{\text{volume}}$$ (typical units: kg/m^3)

7 You can use ratios such as 2:3 and 5:4:7 to show how quantities are divided or shared.

8 Large and small numbers can conveniently be represented in standard form:

$$a \times 10^n$$

where $1 \leqslant a < 10$ and n is an integer
For example,

$$7\,200\,000 = 7.2 \times 10^6$$
$$0.000\,135 = 1.35 \times 10^{-4}$$

Worked examination question 1 [L]

In 1990, a charity sold $2\frac{1}{4}$ million lottery tickets at 25p each.
80% of the money obtained was kept by the charity.

(a) Calculate the amount of money kept by the charity.

In 1991, the price of a lottery ticket fell by 20%.
Sales of lottery tickets increased by 20%.
80% of the money obtained was kept by the charity.

(b) Calculate the percentage change in the amount of money kept by the charity.

Answer

(a) Amount to charity 80% $= \dfrac{80}{100}$

Value of 80% of $2\frac{1}{4}$ million 25p tickets $= \dfrac{80}{100} \times 2\,250\,000 \times £0.25$

$= £450\,000$

(b) Using **2**

new price of lottery ticket = (100 − 20)% = 80% of old price

$= \dfrac{80}{100} \times £0.25 = £0.20$

Using **1**

increase of 20% in sales = (100 + 20)% = 120%

$\therefore$ sales $= \dfrac{120}{100} \times 2\,250\,000$

$= 2\,700\,000$ sales

Amount to charity $= 2\,700\,000 \times £0.20 \times \dfrac{80}{100}$

$= £432\,000$

Using **3** % change $= \dfrac{\text{decrease}}{\text{original}} \times 100\%$

$= \dfrac{(450\,000 - 432\,000)}{450\,000} \times 100\%$

$= 4\%$

Example 1

Calculate the compound interest on £800 at 6.5% over 5 years.

Answer

Using **4** $A = P\left(1 + \dfrac{R}{100}\right)^n$

where $P = 800$

$R = 6.5$

$n = 5$

Then $A = 800\left(1 + \dfrac{6.5}{100}\right)^5 = £1096.07$ to the nearest penny.

So the compound interest is £1096.07 − £800 = £296.07

Worked examination question 2 [L]

The speed of light is approximately 300 000 000 m/s.

(a) Write 300 000 000 in standard index form.
(b) Calculate the time, in seconds, light takes to travel 1 metre.
Give your answer in standard index form.

Answer

(a) Using **8** where $a = 3$ and $n = 8$

3.0×10^8 m/s

(b) Using **5** $\text{time} = \dfrac{\text{distance}}{\text{speed}}$

Remember to keep the units the same throughout the problem.

where distance = 1 metre, speed = 3.0×10^8 m/s

$$\text{time} = \frac{1}{3.0 \times 10^8}$$

$$= 3.3 \times 10^{-9} \text{ seconds}$$

Example 2

Share 1320 in the ratio 5:4:3

Answer

Using **7** There are 12 parts so 1 part = $1320 \div 12 = 110$

$\therefore$ 1320 is shared into: $5 \times 110 = 550$

$4 \times 110 = 440$

$3 \times 110 = 330$

Example 3

In the sales a shop reduces all prices by 20%.
The sale price of a coat is £50.
Calculate the original price of the coat.

Answers

Using **2** the sale price = (100 – 20)% = 80% of the original price.

$\therefore$ sale price = $0.8 \times$ original price

$\therefore$ $\dfrac{\text{sale price}}{0.8} = \text{original price}$

$\therefore$ $\text{original price} = \dfrac{£50}{0.8}$

$= £62.50$

Revision exercise 2

1 A suit is originally marked at a price of £240. It is later increased in price by 12%, then reduced in a sale by 25%. What is the sale price?

2 Calculate the compound interest on £8400 over 6 years at 7.3%.

3 Share £6600 in the ratio 8:4:3

4 Work out the value of

$$(4.6 \times 10^{-2}) \times (8.3 \times 10^{4})$$

giving your answer in standard index form. [L]

5 A Building Society is going to be sold for £1 800 000 000.

(a) Write the number 1 800 000 000 in standard form.

This money is going to be shared equally between the 2.5×10^{6} members of the Building Society.

(b) How much should each member get?

Later, 3×10^{5} members find out that they **will not** get a share of the money.

(c) How many members **will** now receive a share of the money? Give your answer in standard form. [L]

6 The diameter of an atom is 0.000 000 03 m.

(a) Write 0.000 000 03 in standard form.

Using the most powerful microscope, the smallest objects which can be seen have diameters which are **one hundredth** of the diameter of an atom.

(b) Calculate the diameter, in metres, of the smallest objects which can be seen using this microscope. Give your answer in standard form. [L]

7

KILLICK BANK

MONTHLY REPORT JUNE

147 million pounds was used to buy 2100 houses.
Average cost of a house is £

(a) Write the number 147 million in standard form.

(b) Write the number 2100 in standard form.

The corner of the page showing the average cost of a house is missing.

(c) Use your answers to **(a)** and **(b)** to calculate the average cost of a house. Give your answer in standard form. [L]

8 A large supermarket imports wine from France.
A box of 12 bottles of wine costs the supermarket 180 francs per box.
The supermarket sells the wine for £2.40 per bottle.
The exchange rate is 7.50 francs to the £.

(a) Calculate the percentage profit made on each bottle.

The exchange rate changes to 7.20 francs to the £.

(b) Calculate the new selling price per bottle so that the percentage profit remains the same. [L]

9 In the sales a department store reduces all prices by 25%.
The sale price of a dress is £69.
Work out the price of this dress before the sale.

10 The area of the Earth covered by sea is 362 000 000 km^2.

(a) Write 362 000 000 in standard form.

The surface area, A km^2, of the Earth may be found using the formula

$$A = 4\pi r^2$$

where r km is the radius of the Earth.

$$r = 6.38 \times 10^3.$$

(b) Calculate the surface area of the Earth.
Give your answer in standard form, correct to 3 significant figures.

(c) Calculate the percentage of the Earth's surface which is covered by sea.
Give your answer correct to 2 significant figures. [L]

Test yourself	What to review
	If your answer is incorrect:
1 A car priced at £10 400 is increased by 4.5%, then reduced by 10% in the Easter sale. What is the cost of the car at Easter?	*Review Higher book Unit 5, page 94, Example 3 and page 95, Example 4.*
2 A person invests £5000 at 6.6% compound interest over 5 years. What is the total amount after 5 years?	*Review Higher book Unit 5, page 98, Section 5.6.*
3 Share £2400 in the ratio 6:4:2	*Review Higher book Unit 5, page 106, Example 12.*
4 Work out $(4 \times 10^8) - (4 \times 10^6)$ Give your answer in standard form.	*Review Higher book Unit 5, page 114, Example 14.*

Answers to Test yourself

1 £9781.20 **2** £6882.66 **3** 1200, 800, 400 **4** 3.96×10^8

3 Rational and irrational numbers

Key points to remember

1 A terminating decimal occurs when the denominator divides exactly into the numerator.
For example,

$$\tfrac{1}{8} = \tfrac{125}{1000} = 0.125$$

2 A recurring decimal occurs when the denominator divides the numerator giving a repeating pattern.
For example,

$$\tfrac{2}{7} = 0.285\,714\,285\,714\ldots$$

The pattern is repeated every 6 decimal places.

3 Numbers which have decimal parts that either terminate or recur are called rational numbers.

They can be expressed as $\dfrac{a}{b}$ where a and b are integers.
For example,

$$5 = \tfrac{5}{1},\ 0.25 = \tfrac{1}{4},\ 0.66\dot{6} = \tfrac{2}{3}$$

An integer is a positive or negative whole number, including zero.

4 Irrational numbers cannot be written as fractions in the form $\dfrac{a}{b}$ where a and b are integers.
For example:

$$0.232\,332\,333\ldots$$
$$\pi = 3.141\,592\,654\ldots$$

Square roots of prime numbers are irrational.

Irrational numbers do not terminate or have any recurring pattern.

5 The set of real numbers is the set of all rational numbers together with the set of all irrational numbers.

Worked examination question 1 [L]

$3 \qquad 3.14 \qquad \pi \qquad 3\tfrac{1}{7} \qquad \tfrac{142}{45} \qquad \sqrt{10}$

From the list above, write down

(a) the irrational numbers,
(b) two numbers whose sum is rational,
(c) two numbers whose product is rational.

Answer

(a) Using **4** π is irrational.
$\sqrt{10}$ is irrational since $10 = 2 \times 5$ and square roots of prime numbers or multiples of different prime numbers are irrational.
(b) Using **3** $3 + 3.14 = 6.14$
(c) Using **3** Either $3 \times 3.14 = 9.42$
or $3 \times 3\frac{1}{7} = 9\frac{3}{7}$
or $\sqrt{10} \times \sqrt{10} = \sqrt{100} = 10$, etc.

Worked examination question 2 [L]

Write down the recurring decimal $0.\dot{4}\dot{8}$ in the form $\frac{a}{b}$, where a and b are integers.

Answer

Using **2** $0.\dot{4}\dot{8} = 0.48\,48\,48\ldots$
Let $x = 0.48\,48\,48\ldots$ (1)
Then $100x = 48.484\,848\ldots$ (2)

Multiply by a factor of 10 equivalent to the number of recurring digits.
Here, there are 2 recurring digits.
Multiply by $10^2 = 100$.

Then subtract (2) – (1)

$$100x - x = 48.484\,848\ldots - 0.484\,848\ldots$$
$$99x = 48$$
$$x = \tfrac{48}{99} = \tfrac{16}{33}$$

Therefore $0.\dot{4}\dot{8} = \frac{16}{33}$

Worked examination question 3 [L]

(a) Write down a number which is greater than 17 and less than 18 that has a rational square root.
(b) Give an example of two different irrational numbers c and d such that $c \times d$ is a rational number. [L]

Answer

(a) $\sqrt{17} = 4.1231\ldots$
$\sqrt{18} = 4.2426$
Choose any terminating or recurring decimal between these values, say 4.2.
Then $4.2^2 = 17.64$

(b) Using **4** let $c = \sqrt{3}$ and $d = \sqrt{27}$
Then $c \times d = \sqrt{3} \times \sqrt{27} = \sqrt{3 \times 27} = \sqrt{81} = 9$ (rational)

Revision exercise 3

1 Which of the following are irrational numbers?

$\sqrt{6}$ $\quad \frac{4}{9}$ $\quad 0.6$ $\quad 0.4$ $\quad 2\pi$

2 Write those numbers that are rational

$\frac{2}{3}$ 1.6 $\sqrt{5}$ $\frac{4}{17}$ π [L]

3 **(a)** Explain why $0.\dot{1}4285\dot{7}$ is a rational number.

(b) $\sqrt{1}$, $\sqrt{2}$, $\sqrt{3}$, $\sqrt{4}$, $\sqrt{5}$, $\sqrt{6}$, $\sqrt{7}$, $\sqrt{8}$, $\sqrt{9}$, $\sqrt{10}$

Which of these square roots are rational numbers? [L]

4 Write down two examples of

(i) **rational** numbers between 3 and 4

(ii) **irrational** numbers between 3 and 4. [L]

5 Every rational number can be written as a fraction $\frac{a}{b}$

where a and b are integers.

When $x = 0.919\,191\ldots$

then $100x = 91.919\,1\ldots$

(a) **(i)** Work out the value of $99x$.

(ii) Write down x as a fraction $\frac{a}{b}$ where a and b are integers.

(b) Write down a positive rational number which is less than x. [L]

6 An irrational number is multiplied by another irrational number.

(a) Write down an example to show that the answer could be a rational number.

(b) Give an example of two different irrational numbers a and b, where $\frac{a}{b}$ is a rational number.

Test yourself

What to review

If your answer is incorrect:

1 Which of the numbers below are rational?

$\sqrt{30}$, 0.35, $\frac{22}{7}$, $\sqrt{2}$, $\frac{\sqrt{7}}{\sqrt{3}}$, $\cos 60°$, $(\sqrt{5})^3$ [L]

Review Higher book Unit 23, page 420, Sections 23.3 and 23.4.

2 Write down a rational number between 1.2 and 1.25. [L]

Review Higher book Unit 23, page 423, Example 10.

3 Write down an irrational number between 1.2 and 1.25.

Review Higher book Unit 23, page 423, Example 11.

Answers to Test yourself

1 0.35, $\frac{22}{7}$, $\cos 60°$ **2** 1.22, etc. **3** $\sqrt{1.47}$, etc.

4 Upper and lower bounds

Key points to remember

1 If you make a measurement correct to a given unit the true value lies in a range that extends half a unit below and half a unit above the measurement
Sometimes these are called the *greatest* **lower bound** and the *least* **upper bound**.

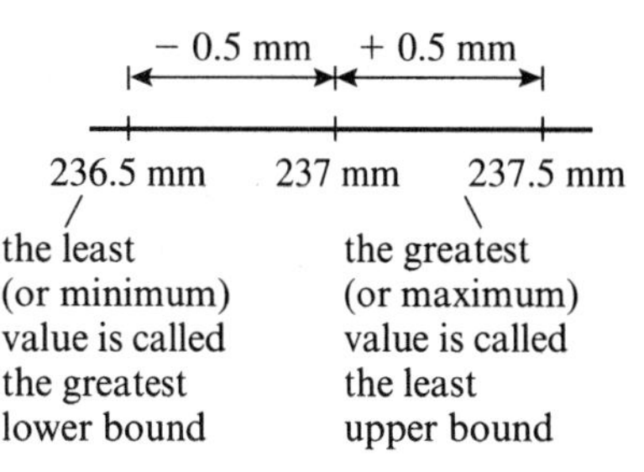

2 The greatest lower bound and the least upper bound are the minimum and maximum possible values of a measurement or calculation.

3 The absolute error is the difference between the measure's value and the actual value of a quantity.

4 The percentage error is found by converting the fraction $\dfrac{\text{absolute error}}{\text{actual value}}$ into a percentage.

Worked examination question 1 [L]

On the scales in Ali's bookshop the weight of a book correct to 2 decimal places is 0.62 kg.

(a) Write down
  (i) the lower bound of the weight of the book.
  (ii) the upper bound of the weight of the book.

Ali needs to work out the weight of 50 copies of the book. He uses his value for the weight of one book.

(b) Calculate
  (i) the lower bound of the weight of 50 books,
  (ii) the upper bound of the weight of 50 books.

(c) Calculate the greatest possible error that could occur in calculating the weight of 50 copies of the book.

(d) Write down the greatest possible error that could occur in calculating the weight of 500 copies of the book.

Answer

(a) (i) Using **1**

$$\text{lower bound} = 0.62 - 0.005 = 0.615\,\text{kg}$$

(ii) Using **1**

$$\text{upper bound} = 0.62 + 0.005 = 0.625\,\text{kg}$$

(b) (i) lower bound 50 books $= 50 \times$ lower bound
$= 50 \times 0.615$
$= 30.75$ kg

(ii) upper bound 50 books $= 50 \times$ upper bound
$= 50 \times 0.625$
$= 31.25$ kg

(c) Greatest possible error
= upper bound 50 books − Ali's value for 50 books
$= 31.25 - 31$
$= 0.25$ kg

(d) Greatest possible error 500 books $= 0.25 \times 10$
$= 2.5$ kg

Example 1

The weight of a bag of sugar should be 1 kg but it is found to have a weight of 1.15 kg.
Calculate the percentage error.

Answer

Using **3** the absolute error $= 1.15 - 1$
$= 0.15$

Using **4** the percentage error $= \frac{0.15}{1.15} \times 100\%$
$= 13\%$

Worked examination question 2 [L]

The radius of the earth is 6400 km to the nearest km. The radius of the sun is 110 (given to 2 significant figures) times the radius of the earth.

(a) Calculate the largest possible radius of the sun.
(b) Calculate the smallest possible radius of the sun.
(c) Using your answers to parts (a) and (b) write down the radius of the sun to an appropriate degree of accuracy.

Answer

(a) Using **1**
upper bound earth = 6400.5 km
largest possible radius of sun = upper bound sun $= 115 \times 6400.5$
$= 736\,057.5$ km

(b) Using **1**
lower bound earth = 6399.5 km
smallest possible radius of sun = lower bound of sun
$= 105 \times 6399.5$
$= 671\,947.5$ km

(c) Appropriate degree of accuracy is where these two values coincide = 700 000 to 1 significant figure

Revision exercise 4

1 Sarah timed a 100 metre race using a stop watch. The time of the winner was 12.6 seconds. The stop watch can measure correct to the nearest one fifth of a second.

(a) Write down the lower bound and the upper bound for the actual time, in seconds.

An electronic timing mechanism gave a time of 12.56 seconds.

(b) State whether this time agrees with that of the stop watch, giving a reason for your answer. [L]

2 A stone is dropped down a well and hits the bottom after t seconds.
The depth of the well, s, is given by the formula

$$s = 4.905 \times t^2$$

(a) When $t = 2.5$ seconds (measured to the nearest 0.1 second) calculate

(i) the maximum depth of the well, given by the formula,

(ii) the minimum depth of the well, given by the formula.

(b) Write down the value of s correct to an appropriate degree of accuracy. [L]

3 The area, correct to 3 significant figures, of a large rectangular car park is 27 500 square metres. The breadth, correct to 3 significant figures, is 155 metres.

(a) Find the possible values of the area and breadth. Use these values to calculate the greatest and smallest length of the car park and hence copy and complete the inequality:

$$\ldots\ldots < \text{length} < \ldots\ldots$$

(b) To how many significant figures are your two answers the same? [L]

4 The area of a circle is found by using the formula

$$A = \pi r^2$$

The radius of a circle was measured wrongly as 4.5 cm.
Then its area was calculated.
The correct measurement of the radius was 4.6 cm.

(a) Work out the error in the calculated area.

Approximations for π include $\frac{22}{7}$, 3.142 and 3.14.
The π button of a calculator is often used instead of these numbers.
A circle has a radius of 4.600 cm, correct to 3 decimal places.

(b) Calculate the upper and lower bounds in which the area must lie for these four values of π and this radius. [L]

5 The length of each side of a regular hexagon is 12.6 cm correct to 3 significant figures. Calculate the **least** length that the perimeter of the hexagon could be. [L]

6 After measuring the length and width of a rectangular piece of card, Perveen draws and cuts out a smaller rectangle as shown in the diagram.

All the measurements are to the nearest cm.

Find

(i) the least possible area of card left.

(ii) the greatest possible area of card left. [L]

7 Correct to 3 decimal places, $a = 2.236$.

(a) For this value of a, write down

(i) the upper bound,

(ii) the lower bound.

Correct to 3 decimal places, $b = 1.414$.

(b) Calculate

(i) the upper bound for the value of $a + b$.

(ii) the lower bound for the value of $a + b$.

Write down all the figures on your calculator display for parts (c) and (d) of this question.

(c) Calculate the lower bound for the value ab.

(d) Calculate the upper bound for the value $\frac{a}{b}$. [L]

Test yourself

What to review

If your answer is incorrect:

1 The length of a rectangle is 135 cm and the width is 85 cm measured to the nearest cm.

(a) Calculate the least upper bound of the width.

Review Higher book Unit 23, page 425, Section 23.7.

(b) Calculate the greatest lower bound of the width.

Review Higher book Unit 23. page 425, Section 23.7.

(c) Calculate the greatest lower bound of the area.

Review Higher book Unit 23, page 427, Example 13.

(d) Give the area of the rectangle to a suitable accuracy.

Review Higher book Unit 23, page 432, Examples 20, 21 and 22.

Answers to Test yourself

1 **(a)** 85.5 cm **(b)** 84.5 cm **(c)** 11 365.25 cm^2 **(d)** 10 000 cm^2 to 1 significant figure

5 Solving equations

Sometimes you will need to solve linear equations, simultaneous equations and equations using graphical methods.

Key points to remember

1 To rearrange an equation you can:

- add the same quantity to both sides
- subtract the same quantity from both sides
- multiply both sides by the same quantity
- divide both sides by the same quantity
- take the square root of both sides

2 Whatever you do to one side of an equation you must do to the other side.

3 Simultaneous equations can be solved:

- graphically, by drawing the straight lines of the two equations and finding the coordinates of the point of intersection.
- algebraically, using elimination or substitution.

4 You can use graphs to solve quadratic and cubic equations.

5 You can use a trial and improvement method to solve an equation by trying a value in the equation and changing it to bring the result closer and closer to the correct figure.

Example 1

Solve the equation:

$$3x - 1 = 4(5 - x)$$

Answer

Using **1** and **2**

	$3x - 1 = 4(5 - x)$
multiply out the bracket	$3x - 1 = 20 - 4x$
add 1 to both sides	$3x = 21 - 4x$
add $4x$ to both sides	$7x = 21$
divide both sides by 7	$x = 3$

Remember to check your answer:
LHS $= 3 \times 3 - 1 = 8$
RHS $= 4 \times (5 - 3) = 8$
LHS $=$ RHS so $x = 3$ is correct

Example 2

Solve $\dfrac{3x}{2x - 4} = 13.5$

Answer

$$\frac{3x}{2x-4} = 13.5$$

Using **1** and **2**

multiply both sides by $(2x - 4)$	$3x = 13.5(2x - 4)$
expand bracket	$3x = 27x - 54$
subtract $27x$ from both sides	$3x - 27x = -54$
	$-24x = -54$
divide both sides by -24	$x = 2.25$

Worked examination question 1 [L]

Solve the simultaneous equations

$$3y = 2x - 5$$
$$y = x - 4$$

Answer

Using **3**

Method 1 Graphically

Choose 3 values for x and work out the values of y for each equation.

x	0	2	4
$y = x - 4$	-4	-2	0

x	1	4	7
$3y = 2x - 5$	-3	3	9
y	-1	1	3

Plot these two straight lines on a grid. The solution is where the two lines intercept, so $x = 7$, $y = 3$

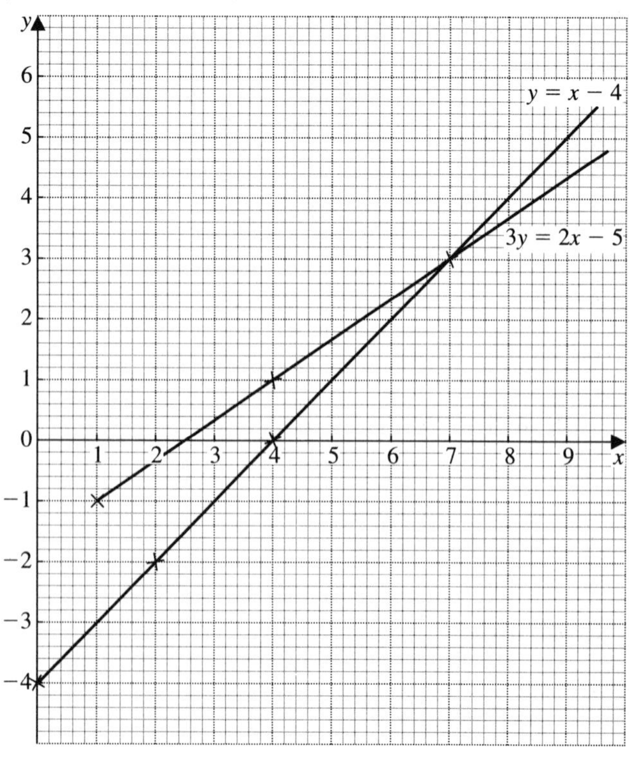

Method 2 Elimination

$$3y = 2x - 5 \quad (1)$$
$$y = x - 4 \quad (2)$$

Do (1) – 2 × (2) to eliminate x

$$3y = 2x - 5$$

Subtract $\quad 2y = 2x - 8$

$$y = 0 + 3$$
$$y = 3$$

Substitute this value into (2) to find x

$$3 = x - 4$$

add 4 to both sides $\quad 7 = x$

So $\quad x = 7$ and $y = 3$

Whichever method you use, remember to check your answer. In equation (1), $3y = 2x - 5$, LHS $= 3 \times 3 = 9$ RHS $= 2 \times 7 - 5 = 9$ LHS = RHS so our answer is correct. To be absolutely sure, check the values work for the other equation too!

Method 3 Substitution

$$3y = 2x - 5 \quad (1)$$
$$y = x - 4 \quad (2)$$

From (2) $\quad y = x - 4$

Substitute $y = x - 4$ into (1)

$$3(x - 4) = 2x - 5$$

multiply brackets $\quad 3x - 12 = 2x - 5$

+ 12 both sides $\quad 3x = 2x + 7$

– $2x$ both sides $\quad x = 7$

Substitute $x = 7$ into (2) $\quad y = 7 - 4$

$$y = 3$$

So $\quad x = 7$ and $y = 3$

Worked examination question 2 [L]

$$y = x^3 - 4x - 1$$

(a) Copy and complete the table of values.

x	-2	-1	0	1	2	3
y		2				

(b) On a grid, draw the graph of $y = x^3 - 4x - 1$ where $-2 \leqslant x \leqslant 5$ and $-5 \leqslant y \leqslant 15$

(c) By drawing a suitable straight line on the grid, solve the equation

$$x^3 - 4x - 3 = -2$$

(d) Using the method of trial and improvement, solve the equation

$$x^3 - 4x - 1 = 30$$

correct to one decimal place. You must show your working.

Answer

(a)

x	-2	-1	0	1	2	3
y	-1	2	-1	-4	-1	14

(b)

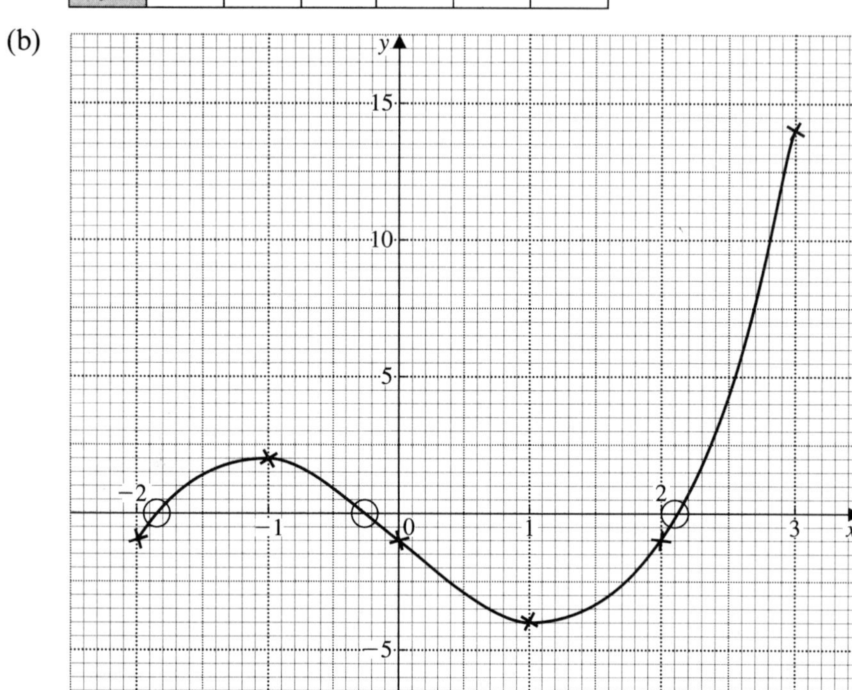

(c) Using **4**

Given $\quad y = x^3 - 4x - 1 \quad (1)$

Solve $\quad x^3 - 4x - 3 = -2 \quad (2)$

To make LHS of (2) the same as RHS of (1), add 2 to both sides of (2)

$$x^3 - 4x - 1 = 0$$

Then compare to equation (1)

So $y = 0$

Draw the straight line $y = 0$ and read off the values where this line intercepts the graph.

Note that the line $y = 0$ is the same line as the x-axis.

This gives $x = -1.85, -0.25$, or 2.1

(d) Using **5**

$$x^3 - 4x - 1 = 30$$

when $x = 3 \qquad x^3 - 4x - 1 = 14$

when $x = 4 \qquad x^3 - 4x - 1 = 47$

Therefore solution lies between $x = 3$ and $x = 4$

try $x = 3.5$	$y = 27.86$	**too small**
try $x = 3.7$	$y = 34.85$	**too big**
try $x = 3.6$	$y = 31.26$	**too big**
try $x = 3.55$	$y = 29.54$	**too small**

Solution is $x = 3.6$ (to 1 d.p.)

Revision exercise 5

1 Solve the following equations

(a) $5x - 4 = 3x + 8$ **(b)** $\frac{1}{2}(4 - 8x) = 5 - 3x$

(c) $3(4x - 5) = 7(x + 3)$ **(d)** $\dfrac{3}{x} + \dfrac{4}{5} = 5$

(e) $\dfrac{35}{3x - 1} = 7$ **(f)** $\dfrac{4x}{5x - 3} = 3$

(g) $3(3x + 1) = 2(9 - 2x)$ **(h)** $\dfrac{3x - 4}{2x + 1} = 2$

2 Solve the simultaneous equations

(a) $2p - 3q = 7$
$p + q = 1$

(b) $3x + 2y = 11$
$x - y = 7$

(c) $4p - q = 15$
$2p - q = 9$

(d) $3x + 2y = 8$
$4x - 3y = 22$ [L]

3 (a) Draw the graph of $y = x^2 - 2x - 2$ and the graph of $y = x - 2$ on the same grid, where $-3 \leqslant x \leqslant 3$ and $-6 \leqslant y \leqslant 15$

(b) Use the graphs to solve the equation $x^2 - 2x - 2 = x - 2$

4 (a) Draw the graph of $y = x^3 - x^2 - 4x + 2$ for values of x such that $-3 \leqslant x \leqslant 3$.

The graph of $y = x^3 - x^2 - 4x + 2$ and the graph of $y = mx + c$, where m and c are constant, may be used to solve the equation

$$x^3 - x^2 - 6x + 2 = 0$$

(b) Find the values of m and c.

(c) Using the values of m and c found in **(b)**, draw the graph of $y = mx + c$ on the grid from **(a)**.

(d) Use the graph to solve the equation

$$x^3 - x^2 - 6x + 2 = 0$$

Give your answers correct to 1 decimal place. [L]

5 (a) Draw the graph of $y = x^3 - 4x + 1$ for values of x such that $-2 \leqslant x \leqslant 2$

(b) Use the graph to find approximate solutions in the range $-2 \leqslant x \leqslant 2$ of

$$x^3 - 4x + 1 = 0$$

(c) By drawing suitable straight lines on the grid, find approximate solutions in the range $-2 \leqslant x \leqslant 2$ of the equations:

(i) $x^3 - 4x - 1 = 0$ **(ii)** $x^3 - 5x + 3 = 0$ [L]

6 Draw the graphs of $y = x^3$ and $y = 4 - x^2$ for values of x such that $-3 \leqslant x \leqslant 3$.
Use the graphs to find a solution of $x^3 + x^2 - 4 = 0$, correct to 1 decimal place. [L]

7 Use the method of trial and improvement to solve the equation

$$x^3 - 4x - 1 = 30$$

Give your answer to 1 decimal place.

8 Use the method of trial and improvement to find the positive solution of

$$x^3 + x = 17.$$

Give your answer to 1 decimal place. [L]

Test yourself

What to review

If your answer is incorrect:

Test yourself	What to review
1 Solve the equation $3(2x - 1) = 7(x + 3)$	*Review Higher book Unit 2, Page 21, Examples 2 and 3.*
2 Solve the simultaneous equations $3x + 4y = 8$, $2y + x = 2$	*Review Higher book Unit 7, page 154, Example 10.*
3 (a) Draw the graph of $y = 2x^2 - 7x + 6$	*Review Higher book Unit 18, page 329, Worked examination question.*
(b) Use the graph to find approximate solutions to the equation $2x^2 - 7x + 6 = 4$	*Review Higher book Unit 18, page 329, Worked examination question.*

Answers to Test yourself

1 $x = -24$ **2** $x = 4$, $y = -1$ **3 (a)**

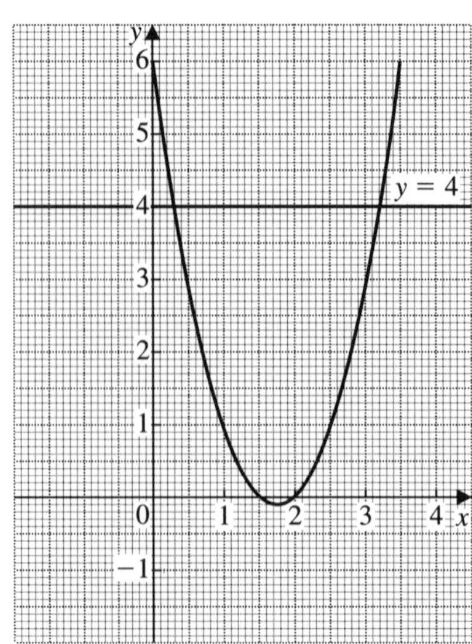

(b) $x = 0.3$ or $x = 3.2$

6 Quadratic equations

Quadratic equations can be used to represent a wide variety of situations. Quadratic equations take the form

$$ax^2 + bx + c = 0, \text{ where } a \neq 0$$

Key points to remember

1 The quadratic equation $ax^2 + bx + c = 0$, with $a \neq 0$ has two solutions (or roots) which may be equal.

2 Quadratic equations may be solved by factorization.

There is more on factorizing quadratics in Unit 1.

3 Quadratic equations may be solved by completing the square.
This rule may help:

$$x^2 + bx = (x + \tfrac{b}{2})^2 - (\tfrac{b}{2})^2$$

4 Quadratic equations may be solved by using the formula:

$$x = \frac{-b \pm \sqrt{b^2 - 4ac}}{2a}$$

5 If $\sqrt{b^2 - 4ac}$ is an integer then $ax^2 + bx + c$ can be factorized.
If $b^2 - 4ac$ is negative there are no real solutions.

6 Quadratic equations may be solved by a graphical method.

Worked examination question 1 [L]

Solve $\quad x^2 - 5x - 14 = 0$

Answer

Using **5**

$$\sqrt{b^2 - 4ac} = \sqrt{(-5^2) - 4(1)(-14)} = \sqrt{25 + 56} = \sqrt{81} = 9$$

Hence $x^2 - 5x - 14$ can be factorized.

$$x^2 - 5x - 14 = 0$$

Look for two numbers that multiply to -14 and add to -5.

Using **2** $\quad (x + 2)(x - 7) = 0$

Then either $\quad (x + 2) = 0$ or $(x - 7) = 0$

So $\quad x = -2$ or $x = 7$

Worked examination question 2 [L]

A rectangular carpet is placed centrally on the floor of a room 6 metres by 4 metres. The distance from the edges of the carpet to the walls is x metres. The carpet covers half the area of the floor.

(a) Show that $x^2 - 5x + 3 = 0$

(b) Solve the equation in (a) to find x, correct to 3 significant figures.

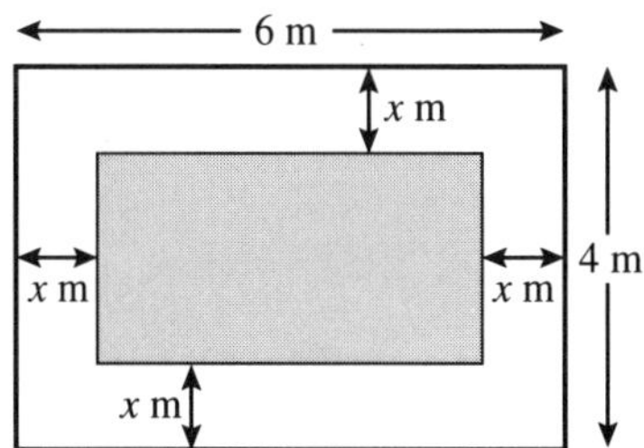

Answer

(a) Width of carpet $= 4 - 2x$
Length of carpet $= 6 - 2x$
Area of carpet $= \frac{1}{2} \times 6 \times 4 = 12$
Area of carpet $= 12 =$ width $\times$ length $= (4 - 2x)(6 - 2x)$

$$12 = 24 - 8x - 12x + 4x^2$$
$$12 = 4x^2 - 20x + 24$$

divide by 4 $\quad 4x^2 - 20x + 12 = 0$

$$x^2 - 5x + 3 = 0$$

(b) Using method of completing the square:

$$x^2 - 5x = -3$$

Using **3** $\quad (x - \frac{5}{2})^2 - \frac{25}{4} = -3$

$$(x - \frac{5}{2})^2 = -3 + \frac{25}{4}$$

Square root both sides $\quad x - \frac{5}{2} = \pm\sqrt{\frac{13}{4}}$

Add $\frac{5}{2}$ to both sides $\quad x = \frac{5}{2} \pm \sqrt{\frac{13}{4}}$

So $\quad x = 2.5 \pm 1.803$

$x = 0.697$
correct to 3 significant figures

When a question asks you to show the answer to a number of decimal places or significant figures, use either completing the square or the formula method.

Or use the formula with $a = 1$, $b = -5$ and $c = 3$

$x = 4.30$ is not a solution as the width is only 4 metres

Worked examination question 3 [L]

(a) Draw the graphs of $y = x^2 - 3x - 2$ and $y = x - 2$ for $-2 \leqslant x \leqslant 5$ on the same grid.

(b) Use the graphs to solve $x^2 - 3x - 2 = x - 2$

Answer

(a)

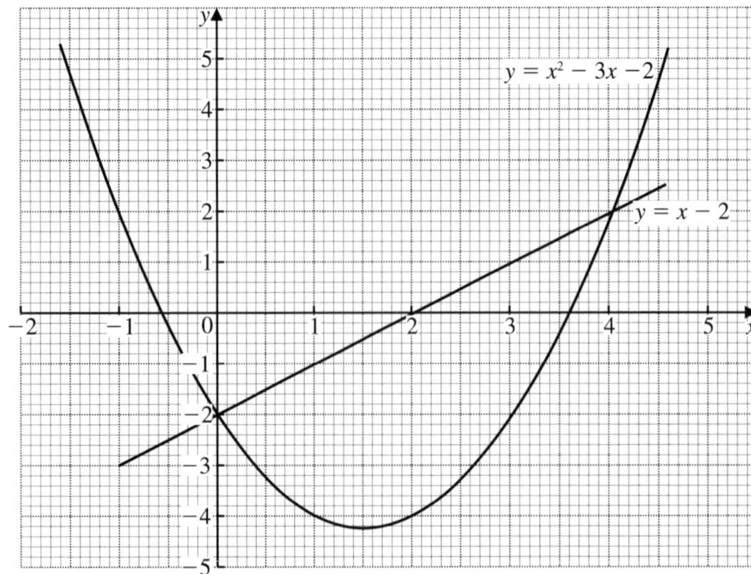

(b) Using **6**, the solution to the equation is where the graphs cross, $x = 0$ or $x = 4$

Example 1

Solve the quadratic equation $2x^2 + 5x - 6 = 0$ correct to 2 decimal places.

Answer

Using **4** $\quad x = \dfrac{-b \pm \sqrt{b^2 - 4ac}}{2a}$ where $a = 2, b = 5, c = -6$

Substitute these values into the rule

$$x = \frac{-5 \pm \sqrt{5^2 - 4(2)(-6)}}{2 \times 2}$$

$$= \frac{-5 \pm \sqrt{25 + 48}}{4}$$

$$= \frac{-5 \pm \sqrt{73}}{4}$$

$x = 0.89$ or $x = -3.39$ correct to 2 d.p.

Revision exercise 6

1 Solve these equations:
(a) $x^2 - 5 = 0$
(b) $x^2 - 7x = 0$
(c) $x^2 + 7x + 12 = 0$
(d) $x^2 - 3x - 18 = 0$
(e) $x^2 + 10x + 24 = 0$
(f) $x^2 - 6x - 16 = 0$
(g) $2x^2 - 5x - 3 = 0$
(h) $5x^2 - 23x - 10 = 0$
(i) $6x^2 + 7x - 5 = 0$

2 Solve the following equations using both completing the square and formula methods. Give your answers correct to 2 decimal places.
(a) $x^2 - 7x = 3$
(b) $3x^2 - 4 = 2$
(c) $x^2 - 3x - 1 = 0$
(d) $2x^2 + 3x - 4 = 0$
(e) $3x^2 - 7x + 1 = 0$

3 **(a)** Draw the graph of $f(x) = 4 - x^2$ for $-3 \leqslant x \leqslant 3$
(b) By drawing a suitable line on the graph find approximate solutions to the equation $4 - x^2 = x$ [L]

4 Fred cycled from home to his friend's house and back again.
The distance from Fred's home to his friend's house is 20 km.
On his way from home to his friend's house, Fred cycled at x km per hour.
On his way back, Fred's speed had decreased by 2 km per hour.
It took Fred 4 hours altogether to cycle to his friend's house and back.
(a) Write down an equation for x.

(b) Show that the equation can be written as

$$x^2 - 12x + 10 = 0$$

(c) Solve the equation in part **(b)**.
Give your answer to 1 decimal place.

Only one of the answers in part **(c)** can be Fred's speed.
(d) Explain why. [L]

5 Rob, taking part in a sponsored walk, walked from Merlow to Fircombe, a distance of 12 km, and then he walked back from Fircombe to Merlow.
Rob's speed on the outward journey was x km/h.
On the return journey he was tired and he walked 2 km/h slower than on the outward journey.
(a) Write down, in terms of x, the time taken for the whole journey.

Rob was walking for a total of $3\frac{1}{2}$ hours.
(b) **(i)** Use your answer to part **(a)** to form an equation.
(ii) Show that this equation can be written as

$$7x^2 - 62x + 48 = 0$$

(c) Calculate Rob's speed on the outward journey. [L]

Test yourself	What to review
	If your answer is incorrect:
1 Solve by factorizing the equation: $2x^2 - 7x - 15 = 0$	*Review Higher book Unit 21, page 380, Example 2.*
2 Solve by completing the square: $x^2 + 5x - 1 = 0$	*Review Higher book Unit 21, page 384, Example 8.*
3 Solve by the formula method: $3x^2 + 11x - 2 = 0$	*Review Higher book Unit 21, page 386, Example 9.*
4 Use a graphical method to solve the equation: $x = x^2 + 2x - 3$	*Review Higher book Unit 21, page 398, Example 18.*

Answers to Test yourself

1 $x = -\frac{3}{2}$ or $x = 5$ **2** $x = -5.19$ or $+0.19$ **3** $x = 0.17$ or -3.84 **4** $x = 1.30$ or -2.30

7 Inequalities

Inequalities are similar to equations and formulae and similar procedures can be applied to solve or represent them.

Key points to remember

1 To solve a linear inequality you can

- add the same quantity to *both* sides
- subtract the same quantity from *both* sides
- multiply or divide *both* sides by a *positive* quantity
- multiply or divide *both* sides by a *negative* quantity and *change* the inequality sign to its opposite.

For example, $2 < 5$ implies $-2 > -5$

2 To solve a quadratic inequality:

- replace the equality sign by = and solve the quadratic equation to give two critical values
- pick a value of x between the two critical values and use it to test the inequality to see whether the solutions lie between the two critical values, or in the other two regions not between the two critical values.

Remember these inequality signs

$\geqslant$ greater than or equal to
$>$ greater than
$\leqslant$ less than or equal to
$<$ less than

Worked examination question 1 [L]

Solve the inequality

$$2x + 5 < 8$$

Answer

$$2x + 5 < 8$$

Using **1**

Subtract 5 from both sides $\quad 2x < 3$

Divide both sides by 2 $\quad x < \frac{3}{2}$

Worked examination question 2 [L]

(a) Draw the straight lines $x + y = 2$, $y = 6$ and $x + 2y = 2$ on a coordinate grid $-6 \leqslant x \leqslant 7$

(b) Shade in the region defined by the inequalities

$$y < 6$$
$$x + 2y > 2$$
$$x + y < 2$$

Answer

(a) Using **2** to draw the line $x + y = 2$, work out 3 coordinates

x	−6	0	7
y	8	2	−5

To draw the line $y = 6$ simply draw a horizontal line across at $y = 6$

To draw the line $x + 2y = 2$ work out 3 coordinates

x	-6	0	7
y	4	1	$-2\frac{1}{2}$

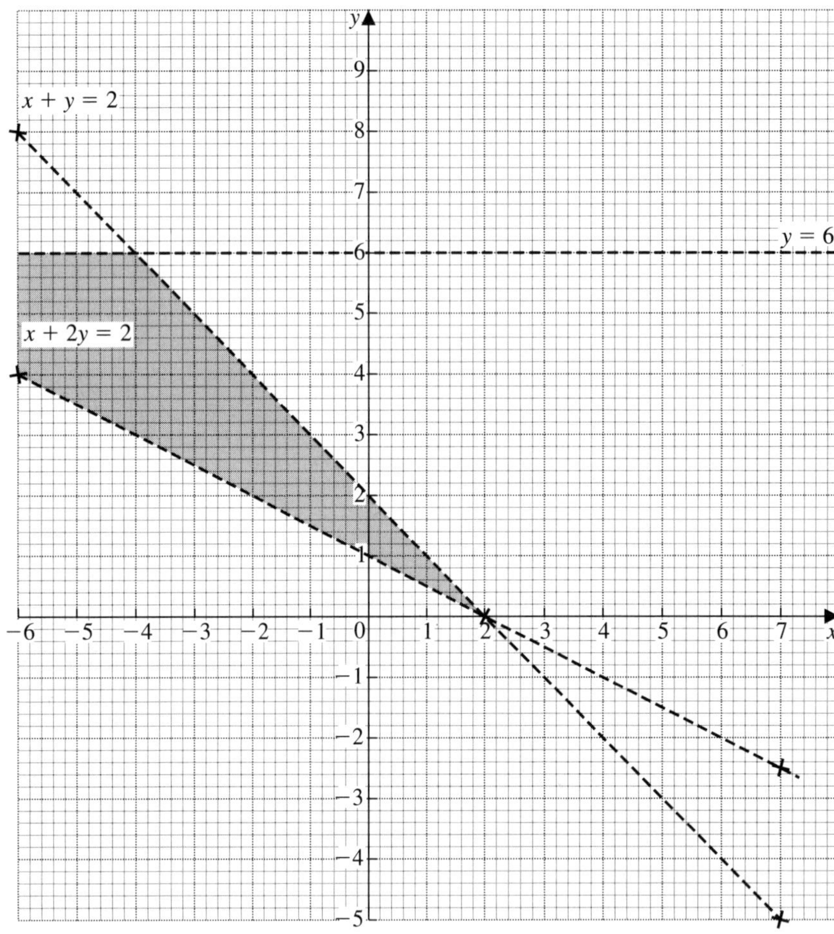

Because $y < 6$, the line $y = 6$ lies in the unwanted region, so it is drawn as a broken line. The other two lines are similarly drawn with broken lines.

(b) Using **2**
choose the region required to satisfy all the inequalities.

Test by substituting a point from within the coordinate grid, say $(-3, 3)$, putting this value in each inequality.

Checking: $y < 6, 3 < 6$ OK

$x + 2y > 2, -3 + 6 > 2$ OK

$x + y < 2, -3 + 3 < 2$ OK

So shade the region bounded by the lines $y = 6$, $x + 2y = 2$ and $x + y = 2$ that contains the point $(-3, 3)$.

Example 1

Solve the inequality

$x^2 < 16$

Answer

Using **2**

replace $<$ by $=$ $\quad x^2 = 16$

square root both sides $\quad x = \pm 4$

Choose a value of x between $+4$ and -4 say 0, then $0^2 < 9$ is true, so x lies in the region between -4 and $+4$, written as $-4 < x < 4$

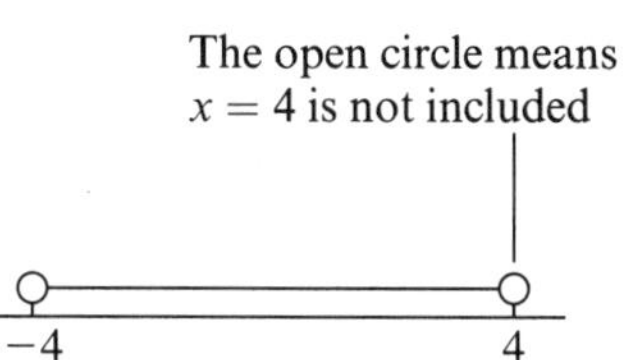

Example 2

Solve the inequality

$(x - 3)^2 \leqslant 36$

Answer

Using **2**

replace $\leqslant$ with $=$ $\quad (x - 3)^2 = 36$

square root both sides $\quad x - 3 = \pm 6$

add 3 to both sides $\quad x = +9$ or -3

Choose a value between 9 and -3, say 0

then $\quad (0 - 3)^2 = 9 \leqslant 36$ is true

So x lies in the region $+9$ to -3, written as $-3 \leqslant x \leqslant 9$

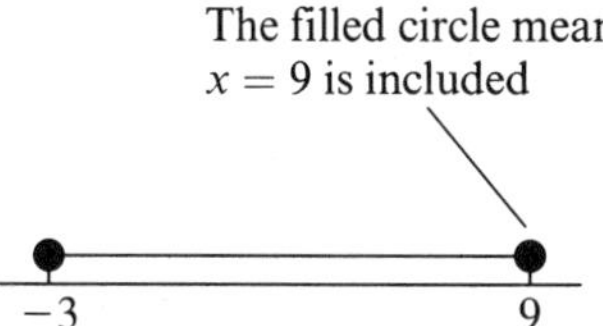

Revision exercise 7

1 Solve these inequalities:

(a) $2x + 3 \geqslant 7$ **(b)** $3x + 2 \geqslant 6x + 1$ **(c)** $-2x \geqslant -9$

(d) $6 - 3x \geqslant 4x$ **(e)** $4 + 5x \geqslant 4x - 2$ **(f)** $4x - 7 \leqslant 8 - x$

(g) $9 - 2x \leqslant 11 - 5x$ **(h)** $13 - 10x > 5x - 12$

2 Draw the straight lines $y = x$, $y = x + 2$ and $y = -2x + 3$ on a coordinate grid.

Shade in the region on your coordinate grid defined by the inequalities $y > x$, $y < x + 2$, $y \leqslant -2x + 3$

3 Shade in the region on a coordinate grid defined by $y < 2x$, $y < 4x + 9$, $x > -2$

4 Solve these inequalities:

(a) $x^2 < 36$ **(b)** $x^2 > 81$ **(c)** $9x^2 < 64$

(d) $(x + 1)^2 \geqslant 49$ **(e)** $(3 - x)^2 < 25$ **(f)** $\dfrac{(3x - 1)^2}{4} < 9$

5 **(a)** Solve the inequality

$$4x + 6 \leqslant 13$$

A sketch of the graph of $y = 4x + 6$ is shown below.

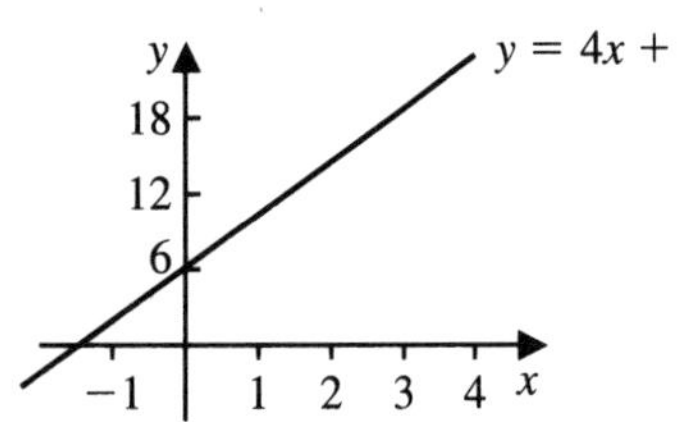

(b) Copy the graph.
By first sketching the graphs of two further lines, shade in the region given by the three inequalities

$x \geqslant 3$ $\quad y \geqslant 13$ and $y \leqslant 4x + 6$ [L]

Test yourself

What to review

If your answer is incorrect:

1 Solve $3x - 7 \geqslant 2x + 8$

Review Higher book Unit 2, page 27, Examples 8 and 9.

2 Shade the region satisfied by $y < 5$, $x > -4$ and $y > 2x + 5$

Review Higher book Unit 7, page 157, Section 7.6.

3 Solve $(5 - x)^2 > 100$

Review Higher book Unit 21, page 395, Example 16.

Answers to Test yourself

1 $x \geqslant 15$ **2**

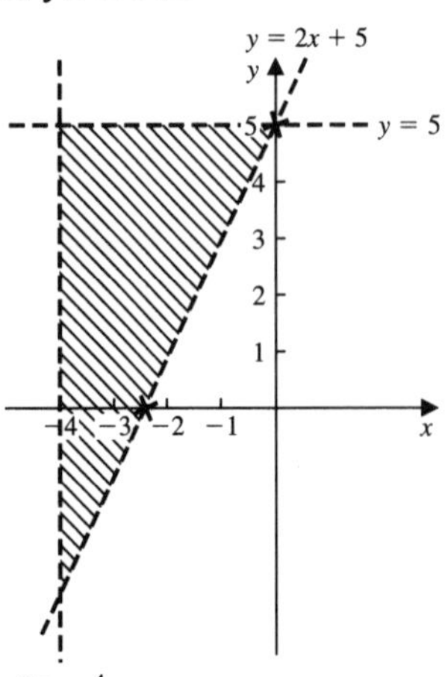

3 $-5 > x$ or $x > 15$

8 Proportion

Key points to remember

1 $y \propto x$ means y is directly proportional to x.

2 When a graph connecting two quantities is a straight line through the origin then one quantity is directly proportional to the other.

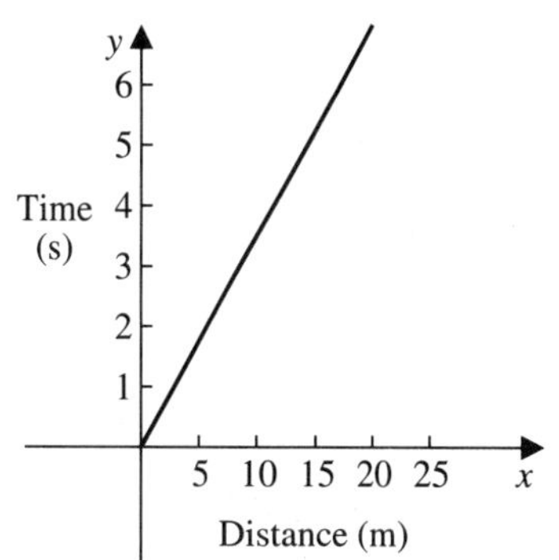

In the graph distance is proportional to time.

3 When y is directly proportional to x:

- $y \propto x$ is the proportionality statement
- $y = kx$ is the proportionality formula, where k is the constant of proportionality.

4 When y is directly proportional to the square of x:

- $y \propto x^2$ is the proportionality statement
- $y = kx^2$ is the proportionality formula, where k is the constant of proportionality.

5 When y is directly proportional to the cube of x:

- $y \propto x^3$ is the proportionality statement
- $y = kx^3$ is the proportionality formula, where k is the constant of proportionality.

6 When y is inversely proportional to x:

- $y \propto \frac{1}{x}$ is the proportionality statement
- $y = \frac{k}{x}$ is the proportionality formula, where k is the constant of proportionality.

Note: the constant of proportionality is often called the constant of variation.

Worked examination question 1 [L]

A ball is dropped to the floor from a height of h centimetres. It bounces to a height of y centimetres.
y is directly proportional to h.

(a) Sketch a graph to show the relationship between y and h.
When $h = 120$, $y = 80$

(b) Find y when $h = 150$

Answer

(a) Using **2**

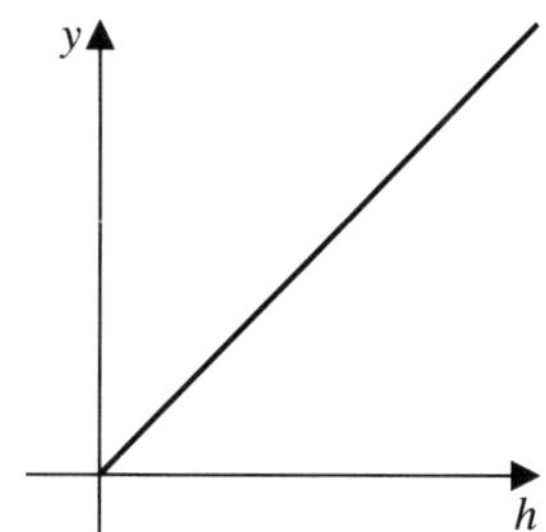

(b) Using **3**

$$y = kh$$

When $h = 120$, $y = 80$
Substitute these values in the formula

$$80 = k120$$

$$\therefore \quad k = \frac{80}{120} = \frac{2}{3}$$

$\therefore$ formula is $\quad y = \frac{2}{3}h$

So when $\quad h = 150$

$$y = \frac{2}{3} \times 150$$

$$y = 100\,\text{cm}$$

Worked examination question 2 [L]

When a stone is thrown upwards with initial speed s metres per second, it reaches a maximum height h metres.

Given that h varies directly as the square of s and that $h = 5$ when $s = 10$

Note: 'h varies directly as the square of s' means h is directly proportional to the square of s.

(a) Work out a formula connecting h and s.
(b) Calculate the value of s when $h = 20$.
(c) Two stones are thrown up. The ratio of their speeds is 3:1. Work out the ratio of maximum heights achieved.

Answer

(a) Using **4** $\quad h = ks^2$

Given $h = 5$ when $s = 10$

$$5 = k \times 10^2$$

$$5 = 100k$$

$$k = \frac{5}{100} = \frac{1}{20}$$

$\therefore$ formula is $\quad h = \frac{1}{20}s^2$

(b) When $h = 20$

$$20 = \frac{1}{20} \times s^2$$

$$20 \times 20 = s^2$$

$$s^2 = 400$$

$$s = 20\text{ metres}$$

(c) We know $h = \frac{1}{20}s^2$

When speed is $3s$ $\quad h = \frac{1}{20} \times (3s)^2 = \frac{9}{20}s^2$

When speed is $1s$ $\quad h = \frac{1}{20} \times (1s)^2 = \frac{1}{20}s^2$

$\therefore$ ratio of heights is $\frac{9}{20} : \frac{1}{20} = 9:1$

Revision exercise 8

1 The cost of toothpaste in a tube is directly proportional to the amount of toothpaste in the tube.
A 100 ml tube costs £1.40.
(a) Find a rule connecting the cost of the toothpaste and amount of toothpaste.
(b) Find the cost of a tube containing
(i) 50 ml **(ii)** 70 ml **(iii)** 135 ml **(iv)** 220 ml
(c) A tube of toothpaste costs £1.75.
How much toothpaste is in the tube?

2 The distance (d metres) travelled by a stone falling vertically varies in direct proportion to the square of the time (t seconds) for which it falls.
(a) Write a formula to connect d, t and the constant of variation k.

A stone takes 2 seconds to fall 20 metres.
(b) Find the value of k.
(c) How far will the stone fall in 4 seconds?

A stone is dropped from a balloon which is 500 metres above the ground.
(d) How many seconds will the stone take to reach the ground?
[L]

3 f is inversely proportional to w.
(a) Find a rule connecting f and w and the constant of variation k.
(b) When $w = 2, f = 1600$.
Find the value of k.
(c) Find f when **(i)** $w = 5$ **(ii)** $w = 0.2$
(d) $f = 5000$, find w.

4 There are two similar saucepans in a kitchen. The smaller one holds 1.5 litres and is 12 cm tall.
The larger saucepan is 16.4 cm tall.
How much will the larger saucepan hold when full?

5 a varies in direct proportion to the cube of b.
(a) Write down a formula to connect a and b and the constant of variation, k.
(b) Given $a = 128$ when $b = 4$, find k.
(c) Find a when $b = 6$.
(d) Find b when $a = 686$.

6 p is directly proportional to q^2.
When $p = 80$, $q = -4$.
(a) Work out the value of p when $q = 10$.
(b) Work out the value of q when $p = 180$.

7 When a car travels at a speed of s m.p.h., its braking distance, b feet, is directly proportional to s^2.
When $s = 20$ mph, b and s are numerically equal.
Calculate the braking distance for a car travelling at 60 mph.

8 The time, t minutes, taken for a satellite to orbit the Earth is inversely proportional to the speed, V kilometres per minute, of the satellite.
(a) Write a formula relating t, V and k, the constant of proportion.

The satellite orbits the Earth every 100 minutes travelling at a speed of 400 Kilometres per minute.
(b) Calculate the value of k. [L]

Test yourself

What to review

If your answer is incorrect:

1 a is directly proportional to b. When $a = 48$, $b = 30$
(a) Work out the rule connecting a and b.
Review Higher book Unit 17, page 310, Example 4.

(b) Work out b when $a = 41$
Review Higher book Unit 17, page 310, Example 4.

2 s is directly proportional to the square of t.
When $s = 5$, $t = 2$
(a) Work out the rule connecting s and t.
Review Higher book Unit 17, page 312, Section 17.6.

(b) Work out t when $s = 425$
Review Higher book Unit 17, page 312, Section 17.6.

3 x is inversely proportional to the square of y.
When $x = 20$, $y = 2$
(a) Work out the rule connecting x and y.
Review Higher book Unit 17, page 316, Example 7.

(b) Find y when $x = 160$
Review Higher book Unit 17, page 316, Example 7.

Answers to Test yourself

1 **(a)** $a = 1.6b$ **(b)** 25.625 2 **(a)** $s = \frac{5}{4}t^2$ **(b)** $t = 18.4$ (to 1 d.p.) 3 **(a)** $x = \frac{80}{y^2}$ **(b)** $y = \pm 0.707$ (to 3 d.p.)

9 Applying transformations to sketch graphs

Key points to remember

1 A function is a rule which changes one number into another number.

For example,

if $\quad f(x) = 3x^2 - 4$

then $\quad f(2) = 3 \times (2)^2 - 4$

$\qquad = 3 \times 4 - 4$

$\qquad = 12 - 4 = 8$

2 The graph of $y = x^2 + a$ is the graph of $y = x^2$ translated a units vertically

- in the positive y-direction if $a > 0$
- in the negative y-direction if $a < 0$

In the diagram opposite, the graph of $y = x^2 + 2$ is the graph of $y = x^2 - 3$ translated by 5 units vertically in the positive y-direction

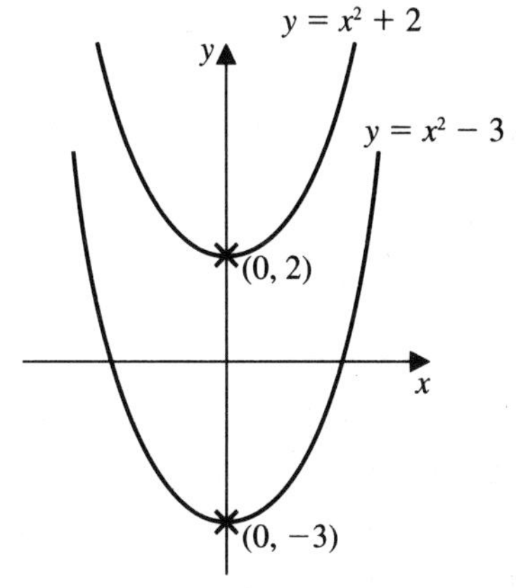

3 The graph of $y = x + a$ is the graph of $y = x$ translated a units vertically

- in the positive direction if $a > 0$
- in the negative direction if $a < 0$

In the diagram, the graph $y = x + 9$ is the graph of $y = x$ translated 9 units vertically in the positive y-direction

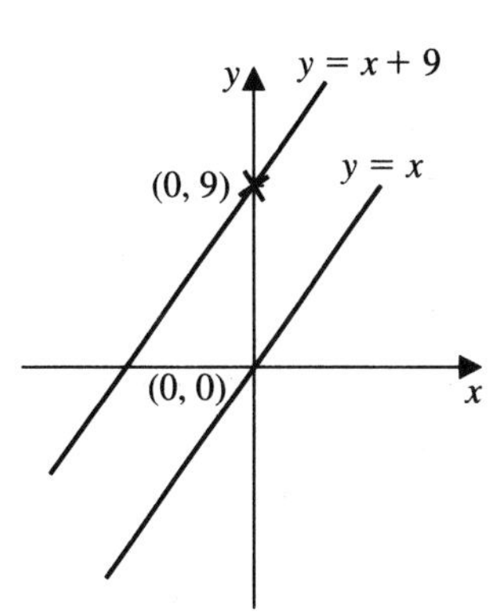

4 For any function f, the graph of $y = f(x) + a$ is the graph of $y = f(x)$ translated a units vertically

- in the positive direction if $a > 0$
- in the negative direction if $a < 0$

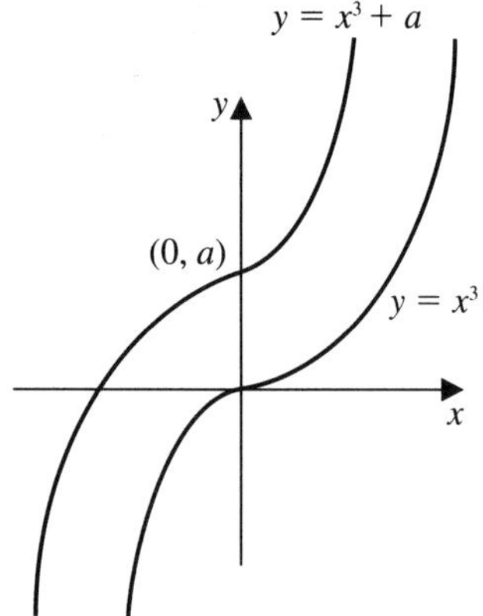

$y = x^3 + a$ is a translation of $y = x^3$

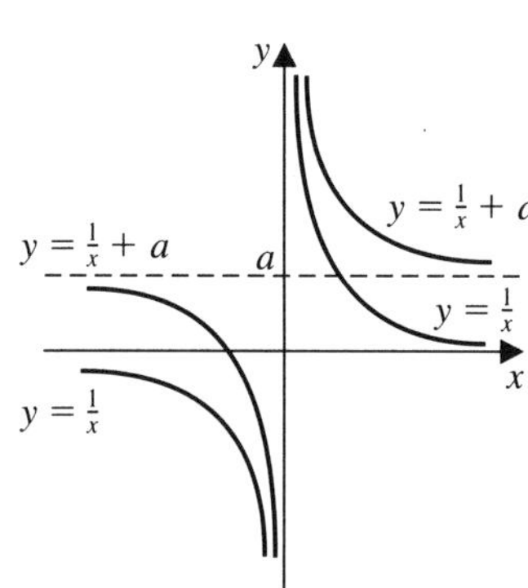

$y = \frac{1}{x} + a$ is a translation of $y = \frac{1}{x}$

5 The graph of $y = (x + a)^2$ is the graph of $y = x^2$ translated a units horizontally

- in the *negative* x-direction if $a > 0$
- in the *positive* x-direction if $a < 0$

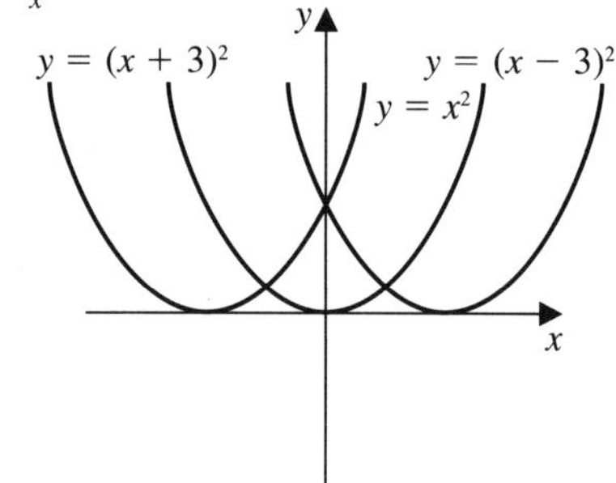

6 The graph of $y = f(x + a)$ is the graph of $y = f(x)$ translated a units horizontally

- in the *negative* x-direction if $a > 0$
- in the *positive* x-direction if $a < 0$

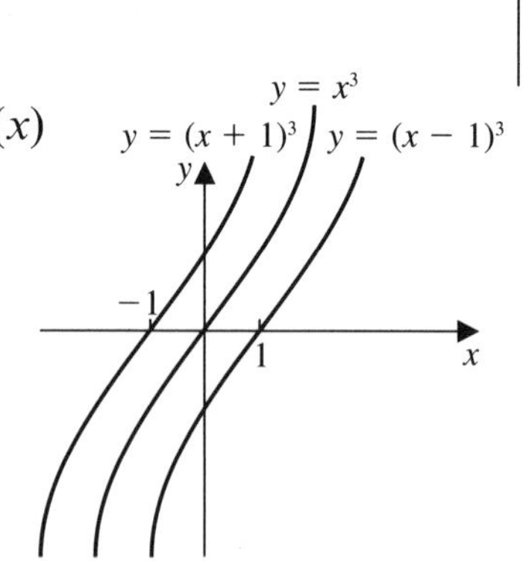

7 The graph of $y = f(x + a) + b$ is the graph of $y = f(x)$ translated a units horizontally

- in the *negative* x-direction if $a > 0$
- in the *positive* x-direction if $a < 0$

followed by a translation of b units vertically

- upwards if $b > 0$
- downwards if $b < 0$

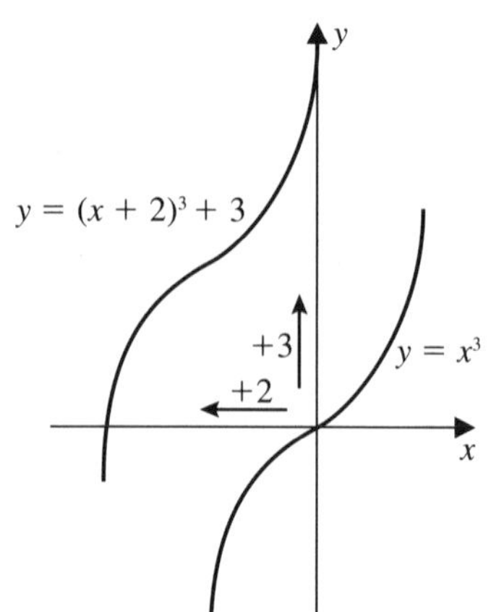

8 For any function f, the graph $y = -\mathrm{f}(x)$ is obtained by reflecting $y = \mathrm{f}(x)$ in the x-axis.

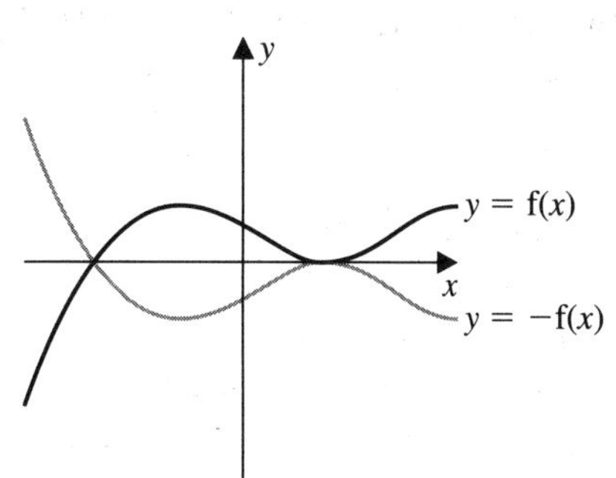

9 For any function f, the graph $y = \mathrm{f}(-x)$ is obtained by reflecting $y = \mathrm{f}(x)$ in the y-axis.

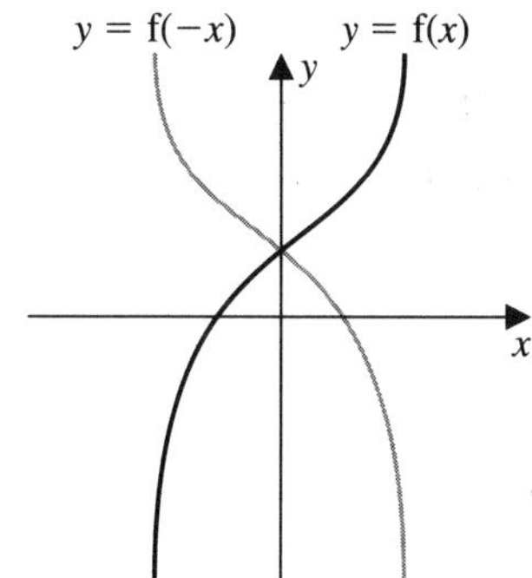

10 For any function f, the graph of $y = a\mathrm{f}(x)$, where a is a positive constant, is obtained from $y = \mathrm{f}(x)$ by applying a stretch of scale factor a parallel to the y-axis.
(Note: the larger the value of a, the steeper the curve.)

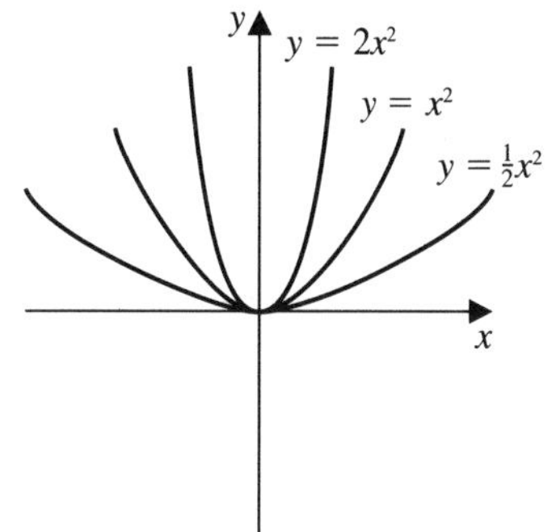

11 For any function f, the graph of $y = \mathrm{f}(ax)$, where a is a positive constant, is obtained from $y = \mathrm{f}(x)$ by applying a stretch of scale factor $\frac{1}{a}$ parallel to the x-axis.
(Note: the larger the value of a, the steeper the curve.)

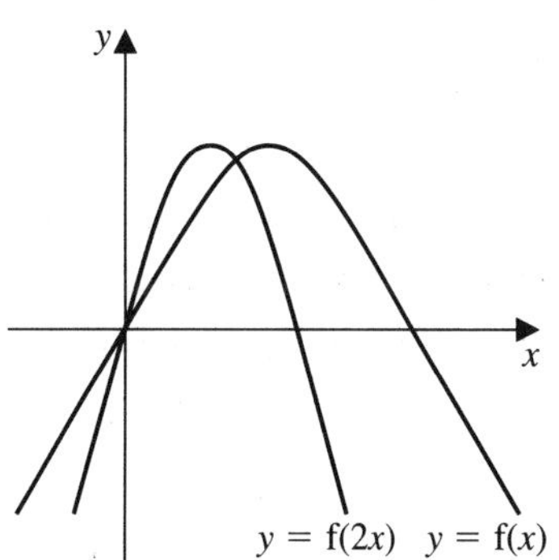

Worked examination question 1 [L]

This is a sketch of $y = \mathrm{f}(x)$, where

$$\mathrm{f}(x) = (x + 3)(x - 2)(x - 4)$$

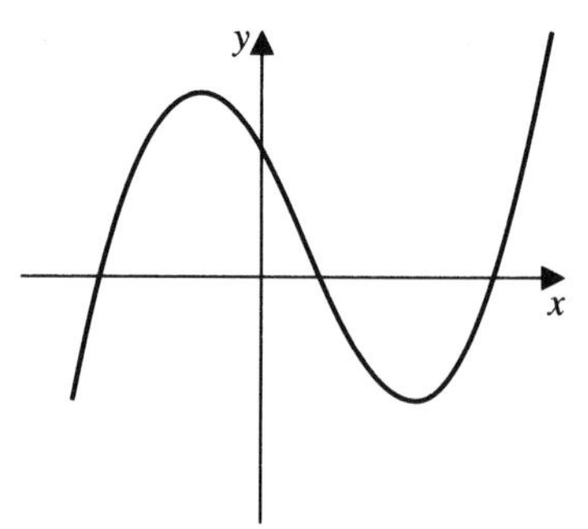

(a) Calculate the value of f(0).
(b) Copy the sketch graph and on the same diagram, sketch the graph of $y = \mathrm{f}(-x)$.
(c) Describe fully the single geometric transformation which maps the graph of $y = \mathrm{f}(x)$ onto the graph of $y = \mathrm{f}(-x)$.

The equation $\mathrm{f}(x) = \mathrm{f}(-x)$ has a solution $x = 0$.
It also has a positive solution x such that

$$n < x < n + 1$$

where n is a positive integer.

(d) Write down the value of n.

Answer

(a) Using **1**

$$\begin{aligned} \mathrm{f}(0) &= (0 + 3)(0 - 2)(0 - 4) \\ &= 3 \times -2 \times -4 \\ &= 24 \end{aligned}$$

(b) Using **9**

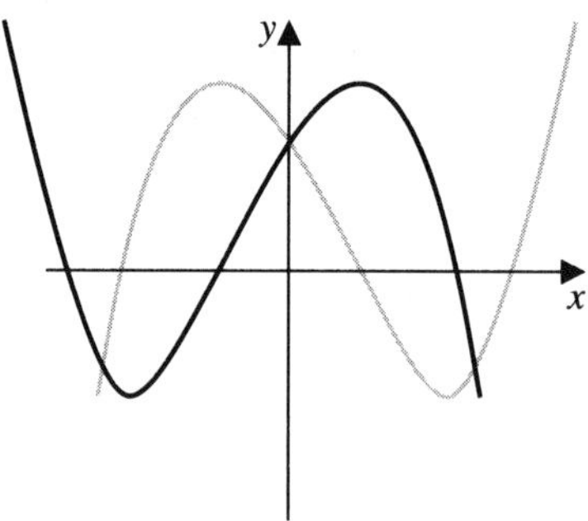

(c) Using **9** reflection in the y-axis.

(d) When $\mathrm{f}(x) = 0$

$x = -3$ or $x = 2$ or $x = 4$

$\mathrm{f}(-x) = (-x + 3)(-x - 2)(-x - 4)$ — To find $\mathrm{f}(-x)$, substitute $-x$ for x in $\mathrm{f}(x)$.

This crosses the x-axis when $\mathrm{f}(-x) = 0$, which is when

$-x + 3 = 0$ or $-x - 2 = 0$ or $-x - 4 = 0$

$x = 3$ or $x = -2$ or $x = -4$

The positive solution is where the two graphs intersect.
From the graph this value lies between $x = 3$ and $x = 4$.
So $n = 3$.

Worked examination question 2 [L]

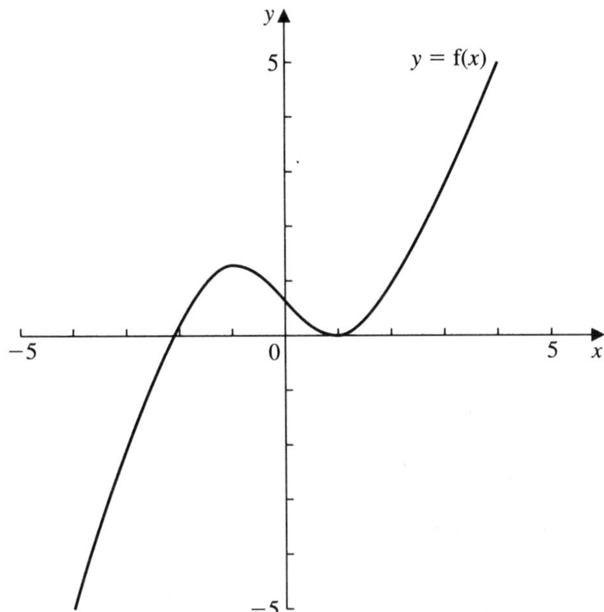

The graph of $y = \mathrm{f}(x)$ has been drawn on the diagram.
Copy the diagram above and sketch the graph of $y = \mathrm{f}(x - 2)$.

Answer

Using **6**

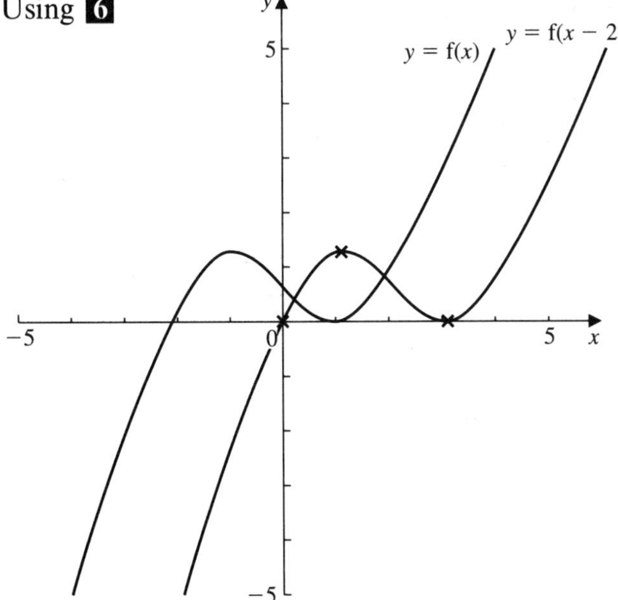

Revision exercise 9

1 $$\mathrm{f}(x) = 5x^2 - 3$$

Find **(a)** f(0) **(b)** f(1) **(c)** f(−2) **(d)** f(5)

2 A graph of $y = \mathrm{f}(x)$ has been drawn on the grid below.

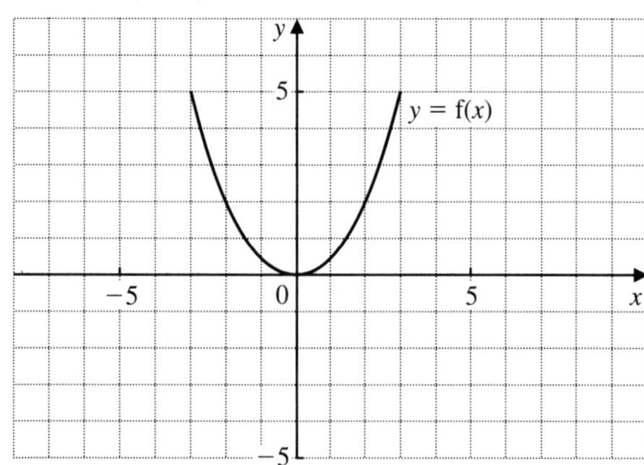

(a) Copy the graph and sketch the graph of $y = \mathrm{f}(x) - 4$.
(b) On the same grid sketch the graph of $y = \mathrm{f}(x - 4)$. [L]

3 The graph of $y = \mathrm{f}(x)$, where $\mathrm{f}(x) = 4 - x^2$ is drawn opposite for $-3 \leqslant x \leqslant 3$.

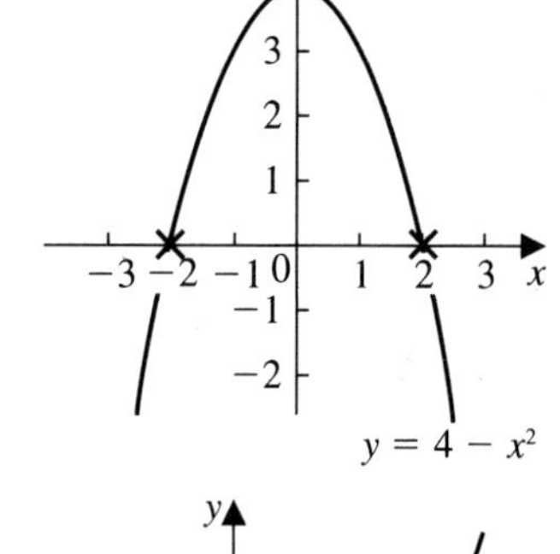

(a) Explain how you would use the graph of $y = \mathrm{f}(x)$ to draw the graph
  (i) $y = \mathrm{f}(x) - 1$
  (ii) $y = \mathrm{f}(x + 1)$
  Sketch the graphs in **(i)** and **(ii)**.
(b) Sketch the graph of $y = -\mathrm{f}(x)$.
  Your graph should include the coordinates of the points where the graph crosses the axes. [L]

4 A sketch of the graph of $y = x^2$ is drawn opposite.

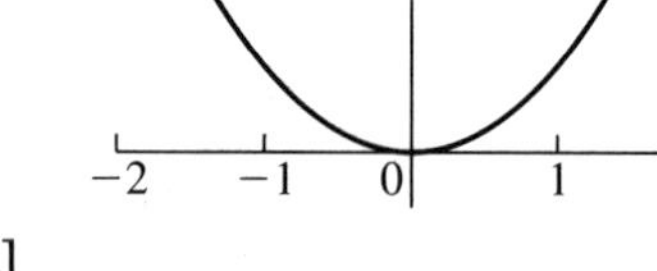

(a) Copy the graph and sketch a graph of $y = (x + 1)^2$.

The two graphs intersect at one point.
(b) Calculate the x-coordinate of the point of intersection.

Two points on the graph of $y = (x + 1)^2$ are at a distance of 9 units from the x-axis.
(c) Calculate the x-coordinates of these two points. [L]

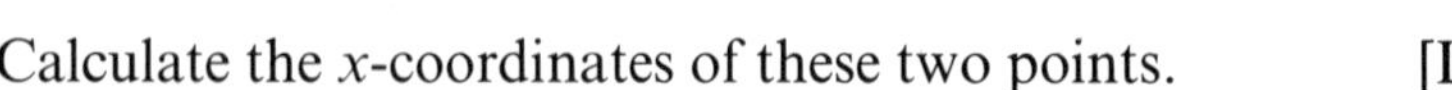

5 Sketch the graphs of $y = \dfrac{1}{x}$ and $y = \dfrac{1}{x} - 2$ on the same grid.

6 Sketch the graphs of $y = x^2$ and $y = (x + 1)^2 + 3$ on the same grid.

7 **(a)** Sketch the graph given by the function
$$\mathrm{f}(x) = (x + 1)(x - 1)(x + 3)$$
on a grid.
(b) On the same grid sketch $-\mathrm{f}(x)$.
(c) What transformation maps $\mathrm{f}(x)$ on to $-\mathrm{f}(x)$?

8 Sketch the graph of $y = 2\cos 3x$ for $-180° \leqslant x \leqslant 180°$.

There is more on trigonometric curves in Unit 15.

Test yourself | What to review

1 $f(x) = x^3 - 3$
Find f(−4)

If your answer is incorrect:

Review Higher book Unit 24, page 436, Example 1.

---

2 Sketch on the same grid
$f(x) = x^3$ and $f(x) = x^3 - 3$

Review Higher book Unit 24, page 438, Section 24.2.

---

3 The graph shows the function $y = f(x)$.

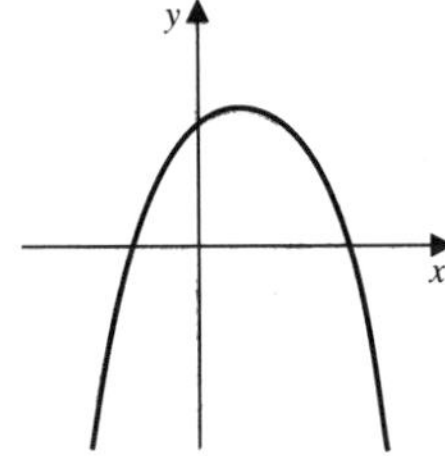

(a) Sketch the graph of $y = f(-x)$

Review Higher book Unit 24, page 449, Section 24.5.

(b) What single transformation maps $f(x)$ onto $f(-x)$?

Review Higher book Unit 24, page 449, Section 24.5.

---

4 Sketch the graph of $y = 2\sin 4x$ for $-180° \leqslant x \leqslant 180°$

Review Higher book, page 456, Section 24.7.

Answers to Test yourself

1 −67

2

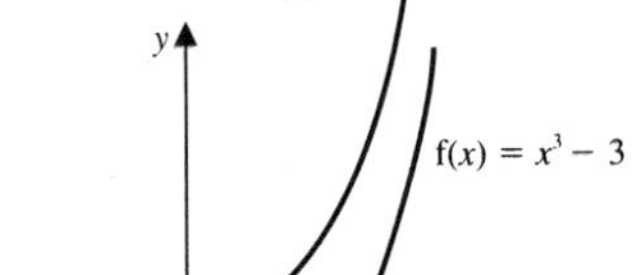

3 (a)

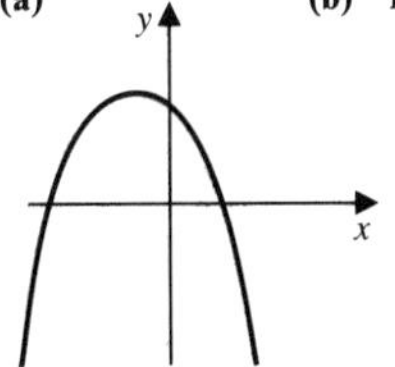

(b) Reflection in the y-axis.

4

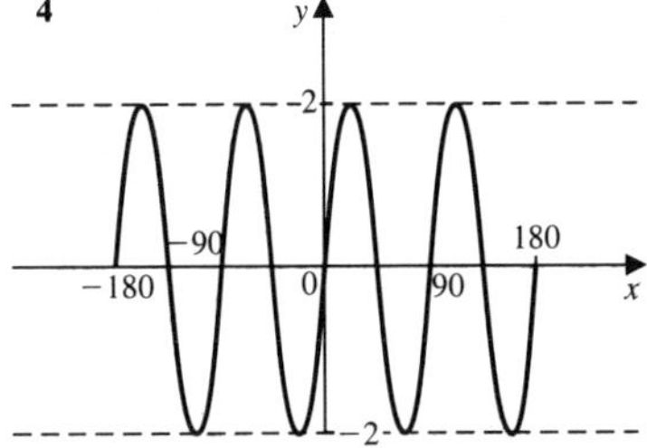

10 Rates of change and areas under graphs

The gradient of a curve describes the rate of change.
The area under a graph may describe quantities such as distance travelled.

Key points to remember

1 A line which touches a curve at a point P is a tangent to the curve at P.

2 The gradient of a curve at a point P is the same as the gradient of the tangent to the curve at P.

3 The rate of change of y with respect to x at a point P on a curve is found by calculating the gradient of the curve at P.

$$\text{gradient} = \frac{\text{rise}}{\text{tread}} \text{ or } \frac{y_2 - y_1}{x_2 - x_1}$$

4 If the gradient is negative then y is decreasing as x is increasing.
If the gradient is positive then y is increasing as x is increasing.

5 The area under a curved graph can be estimated by splitting it up into rectangles and finding the mean of the areas of the upper and lower bounds.

6 The area under a graph can be found by using the trapezium rule.

$$\text{Area} \simeq \tfrac{1}{2}h(y_0 + 2y_1 + 2y_2 + \ldots + 2y_{n-1} + y_n)$$

where h is the width of the intervals and $y_0, y_1, \ldots, y_n$ are the lengths of the parallel sides of the trapeziums.

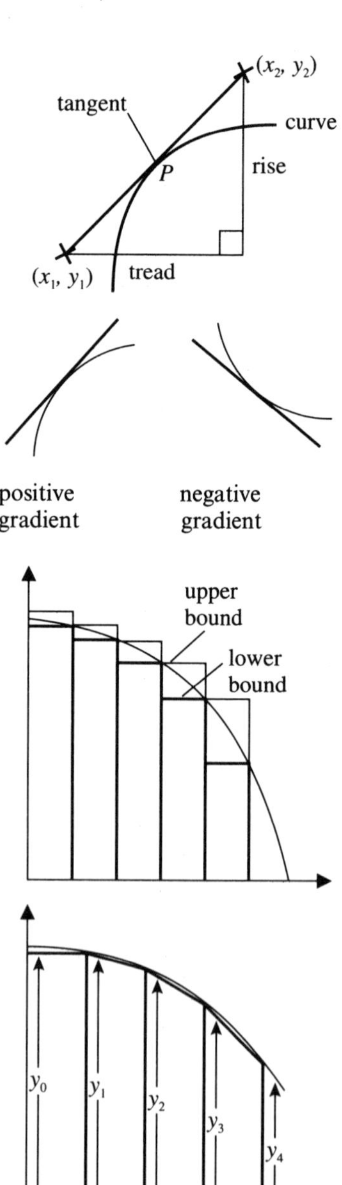

7 Displacement has direction and magnitude.
Distance has magnitude only.

8 Velocity is defined as the rate of change of displacement with respect to time.

9 On a displacement–time graph, the gradient at a point gives the velocity of the object at that point.

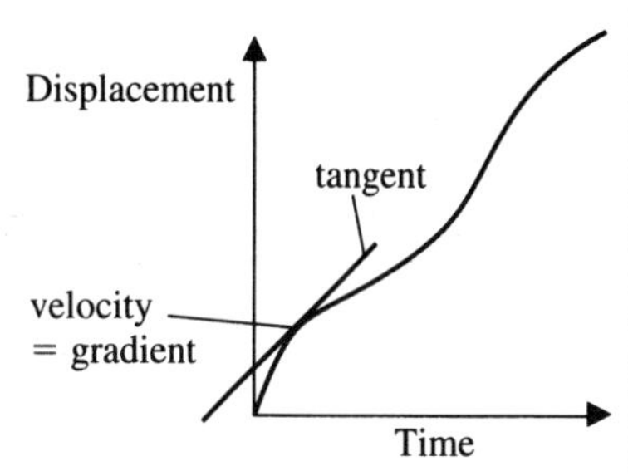

10 Acceleration is defined as the rate of change of velocity with respect to time.

11 On a velocity–time graph, the gradient at a point gives the acceleration of the object.

12 The area bounded by a velocity–time graph and the time-axis gives the distance travelled.

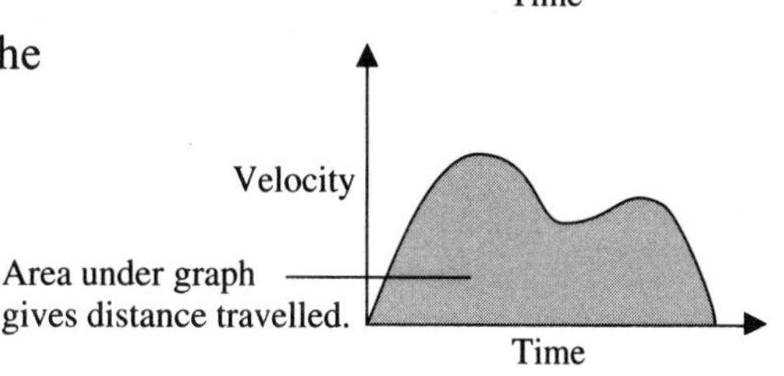

Worked examination question 1 [L]

The graph shows the velocity v metres per second of a car t seconds after it joins a busy main road.

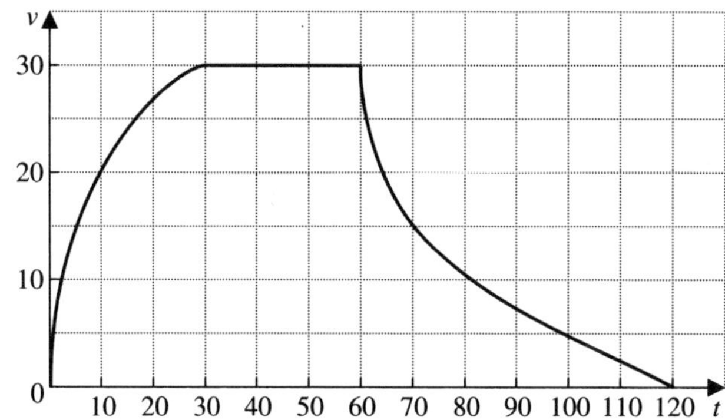

(a) Calculate the acceleration of the car 10 seconds after it joins the busy main road.
(b) Calculate an estimate of the total distance travelled by the car in the two minutes shown in the graph.

Answer

(a) Using **11**

The gradient at the point of the curve after 10 seconds gives the acceleration. So using **2**, draw the tangent to the curve at that point.

Using **3**

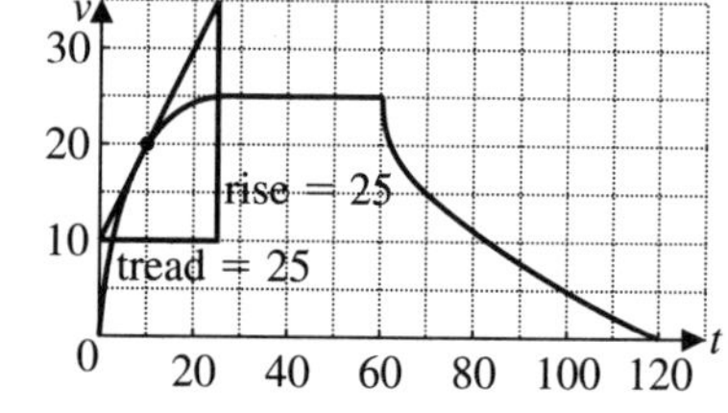

$$\text{gradient} = \frac{\text{rise}}{\text{tread}} = \frac{\text{increase in velocity}}{\text{increase in time}}$$

$$= \tfrac{25}{25} = 1\,\text{m}\,\text{s}^{-2}$$

(b) Using **12**

Area under curve is the distance.

Using method **5**

Splitting into rectangles, choose width of rectangle on the time axis = 20 seconds

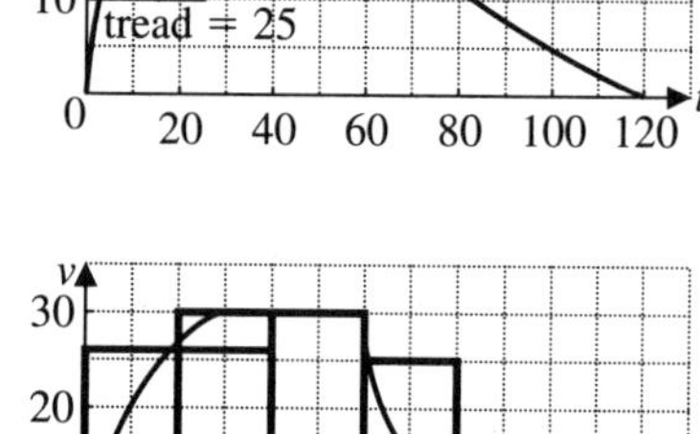

Then sum of the areas of longer rectangles

$= 20 \times 26 + 20 \times 30 + 20 \times 30$
$\quad + 20 \times 25 + 20 \times 10 + 20 \times 5$
$= 2520$

sum of the areas of shorter rectangles

$= 20 \times 0 + 20 \times 26$
$\quad + 20 \times 30 + 20 \times 10 + 20 \times 5 + 20 \times 0$
$= 1420$

The mean of the larger and smaller

$$= \frac{2520 + 1420}{2}$$

$= 1970$ metres

Worked examination question 2 [L]

The speed time graph of a vehicle during the final minute of a journey is shown opposite.
Calculate the total distance travelled by the vehicle in this minute.

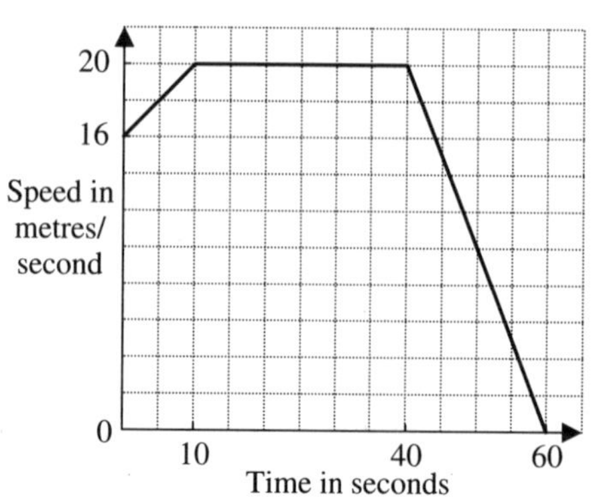

Answer

Using **12**

distance travelled is area under the graph

Using **6**

Using trapezium rule to calculate this area with width of interval $h = 10$ and

$y_0 = 16, y_1 = 20, y_2 = 20, y_3 = 20, y_4 = 20, y_5 = 10, y_6 = 0$

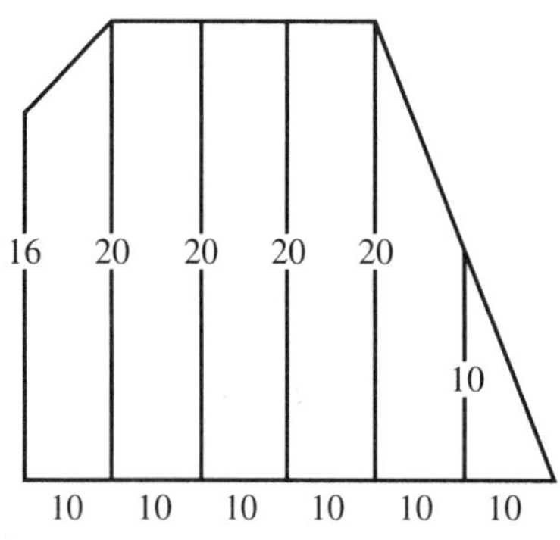

Trapezium rule is:

$$\begin{aligned}\text{Area} &= \tfrac{1}{2}h(y_0 + 2y_2 + 2y_3 + 2y_4 + 2y_5 + y_6)\\ &= \tfrac{1}{2} \times 10(16 + 2 \times 20 + 2 \times 20 + 2 \times 20\\ &\qquad + 2 \times 20 + 2 \times 10 + 0)\\ &= 5(16 + 40 + 40 + 40 + 40 + 20)\\ &= 5 \times 196\\ &= 980\end{aligned}$$

Distance travelled = 980 m.

Revision exercise 10

1

(a) Copy the diagram above and draw the tangent at P to the curve.

(b) Calculate the gradient of the tangent you have drawn. Give your answer to 1 d.p. [L]

2 Draw the graph of $y = x^2 - 3x - 2$

Calculate an estimate of the gradient of the curve $y = x^2 - 3x - 2$ at the point where $x = 2.5$ [L]

3

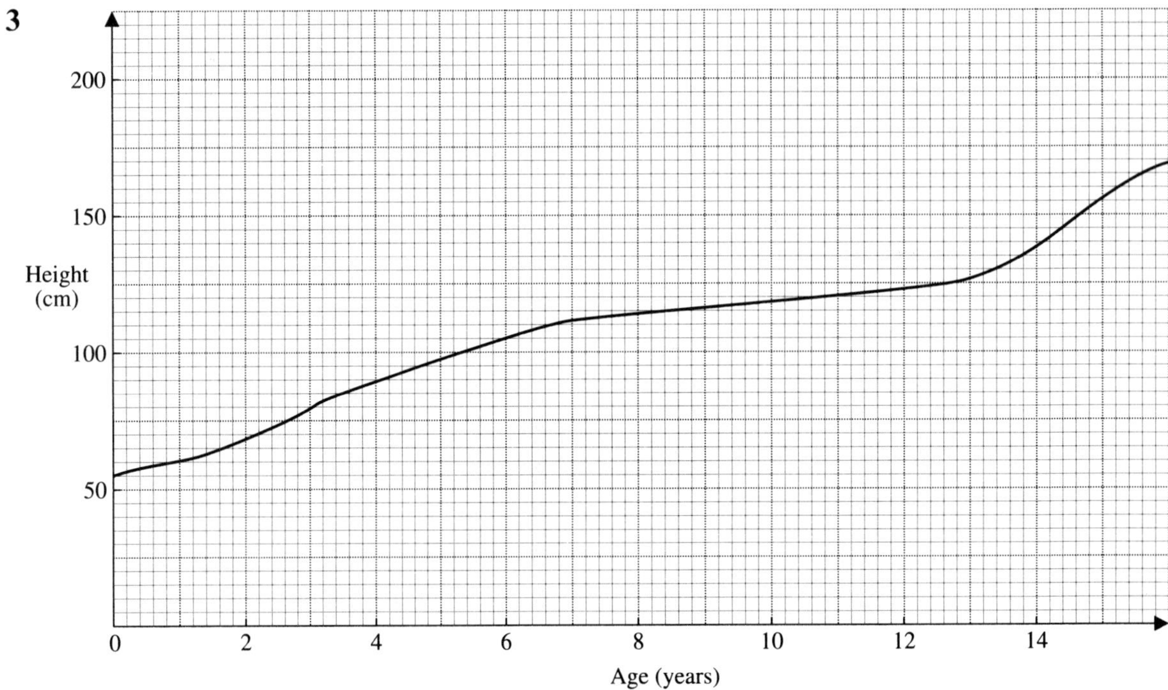

The graph shows how Narinder's height increased in the first 16 years of his life.

(a) Calculate an estimate for the gradient of the graph when Narinder was 14 years old.

(b) What does the gradient represent? [L]

4

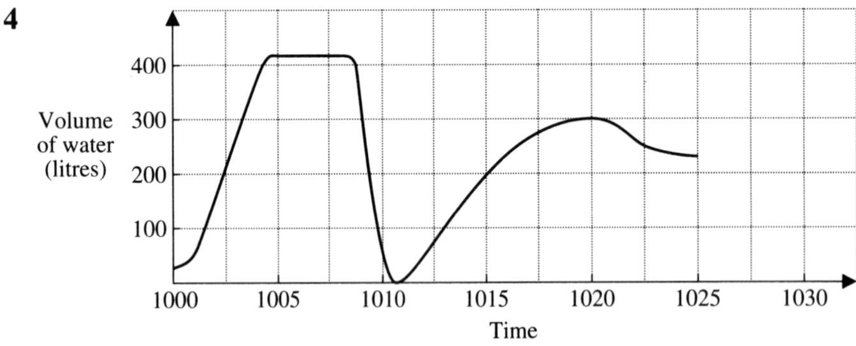

The sketch graph above shows the volume of water in a water tank between 1000 and 1025.

During the morning, the water tank emptied itself completely.

(a) At what time was the water tank empty?

(b) Between which times was the volume of water in the water tank constant?

(c) Between which times was the volume of water in the water tank increasing at its greatest rate? [L]

5

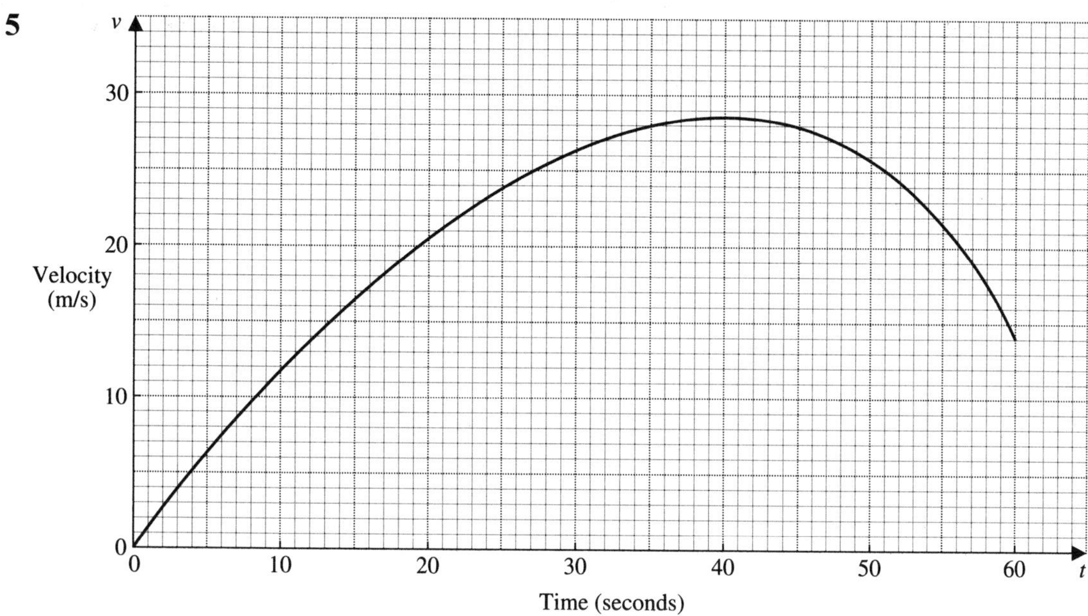

The first minute of a car's journey is represented by the velocity time graph.

(a) Use the graph to calculate an estimate for the acceleration of the car at time $t = 30$ seconds. [L]

(b) Calculate the distance travelled in the first 60 seconds.

6 The graph represents the velocity of a car for a period of 35 seconds.

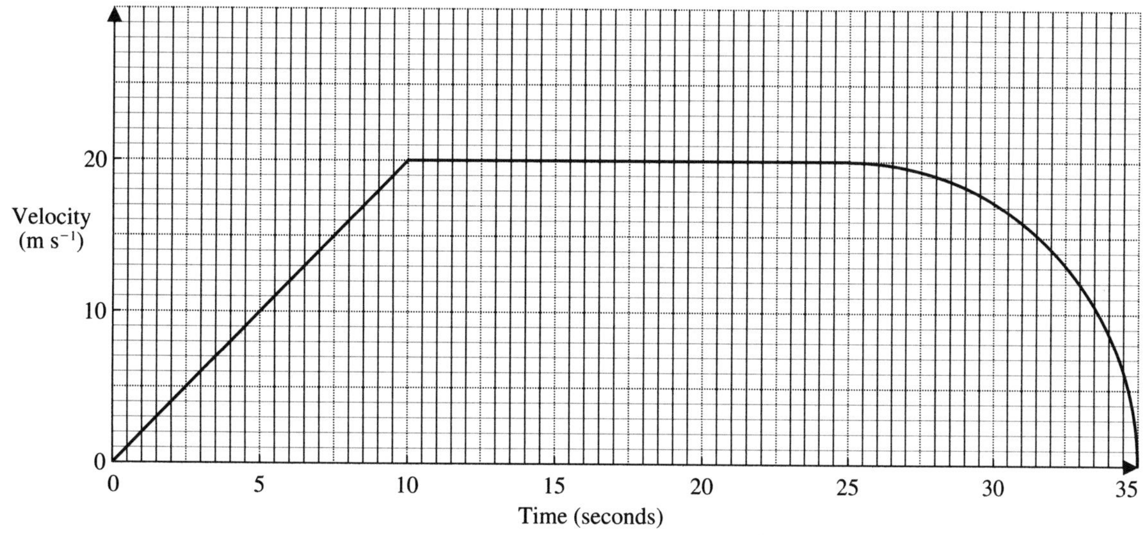

(a) Calculate the gradient of the curve at the time $t = 30$

(b) Explain what this gradient represents. [L]

(c) Calculate the distance travelled.

Test yourself | What to review

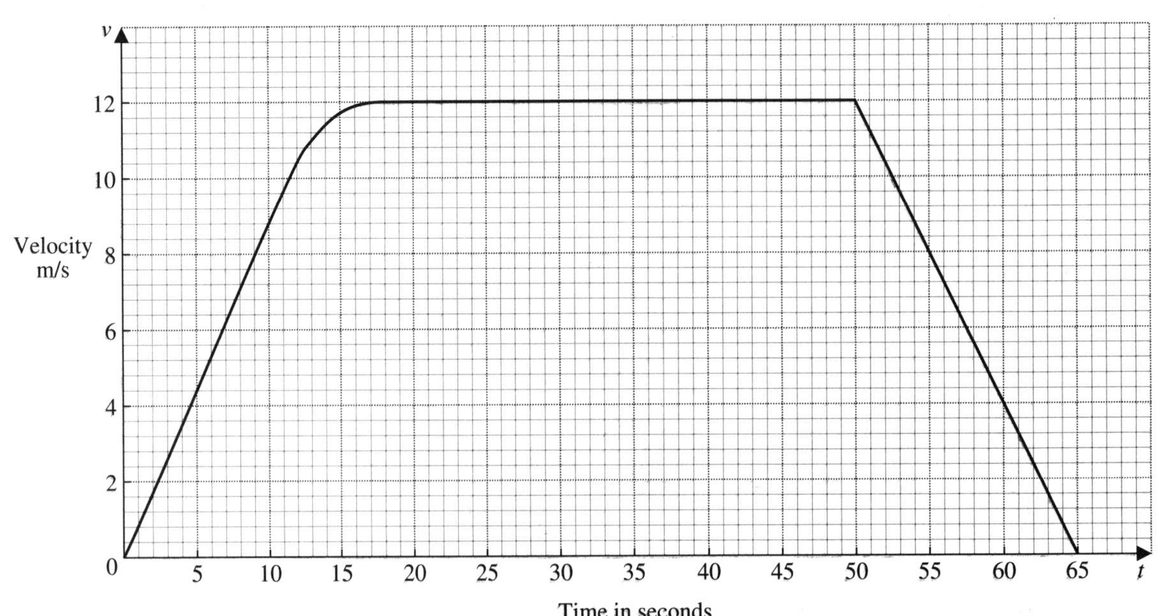

If your answer is incorrect:

1 A car travels between two sets of traffic lights.
The diagram represents the velocity/time graph of the car.
The car leaves the first set of traffic lights.

(a) Use the graph to find the velocity of the car after 15 seconds.

Remember to read this value off the graph when $t = 15$.

(b) Calculate an estimate for the acceleration of the car, in m s^{-2}, after 10 seconds.

Review Higher book Unit 27, page 498, Example 10.

(c) Calculate the distance travelled.

Review Higher book Unit 27, page 499, Example 11.

Answers to Test yourself

1 **(a)** $11.75\,\text{m s}^{-1}$ **(b)** $0.88\,\text{m s}^{-2}$ **(c)** 598 m

11 Modelling

Solving real life problems mathematically and obtaining relationships between two sets of data is called mathematical modelling.

Key points to remember

1 The function $f(x) = a^x$, where a is a positive constant and x is a variable, is called an exponential function.

- If $a > 1$ then a^x is an example of exponential growth with a multiplier of a.
- If $0 < a < 1$ then a^x is an example of exponential decay with a multiplier of a.

2 A point lies on a curve if the coordinates of the point satisfy the equation of the curve.

3 To determine if the experimental results satisfy a given formula, reduce the formula to the form $Y = mX + c$. Plot Y against X and if the points lie approximately on a straight line the formula is confirmed.

- To test $y = px + q$, plot y against x
- To test $y = px^2 + q$, plot y against x^2
- To test $y = px^2 + qx$, plot $\frac{y}{x}$ against x

Then if the points lie approximately on a straight line

- p is the gradient
- q is the intercept

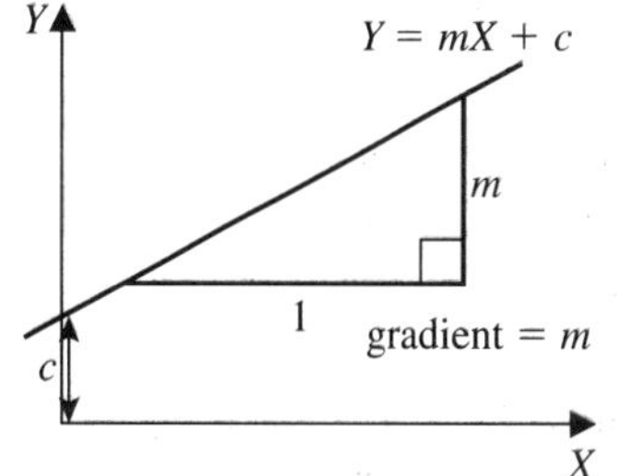

Example 1

The table shows the value of a computer after each year

(y) Year	0	1	2	3	4	5	6
(v) Value	1500	1000	667	444	296	198	132

It is thought the relationship between y and v is of the form $v = pq^y$

(a) Draw a graph of y against v.

(b) Use your graph to find p and q and state the relationship between y and v.

(c) What type of relationship is shown?

Answer

(a)

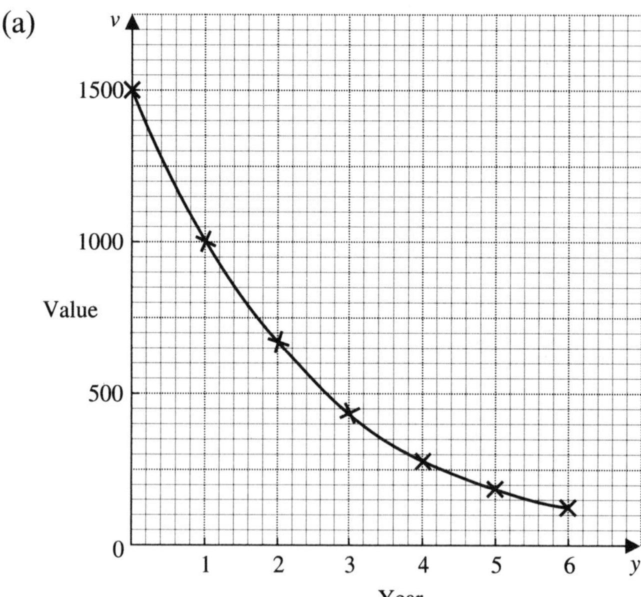

(b) Using **2**

Choose two points, say (0, 1500) and (1, 1000)

These must satisfy $v = pq^y$

Substitute (0, 1500) $1500 = pq^0$

so $1500 = p \times 1$

so $p = 1500$

Substitute (1, 1000) $1000 = pq$

But $p = 1500$ so $1000 = 1500\,q$

so $q = \frac{2}{3}$

so $v = 1500\,(\frac{2}{3})^y$

(c) Using **1** this type of relationship is exponential decay.

Worked examination question [L]

The table shows the distance, s metres, travelled by an object from the point P in t seconds.

t (seconds)	0.5	1.0	1.5	2.0	2.5
s (metres)	1.125	1.2	1.325	1.5	1.725

It is thought the relationship between s and t has the form $s = at^2 + b$, where a and b are constants.

(a) Confirm the relationship by plotting a suitable graph.

(b) Use the graph to estimate the values of a and b.

Answer

(a) Using **3**

Compare $s = at^2 + b$

with $Y = mX + c$

then $Y = s$; $X = t^2$; $m = a$, and $c = b$

Plotting s on the vertical axis and t^2 on the horizontal axis should lead to a straight line to confirm the relationship.

Using the values of t in the given table to find t^2, form a table of values of t^2 against s.

t^2	0.25	1	2.25	4	6.25
s	1.125	1.2	1.325	1.5	1.725

Draw a graph using these values.

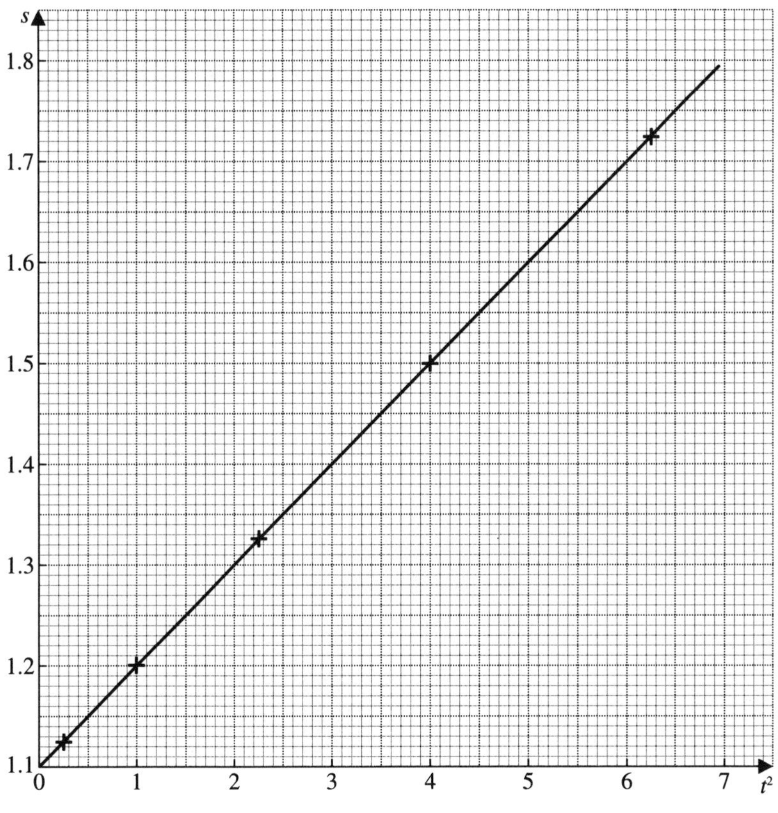

The points do not always lie exactly on a straight line. You may need to draw a line of best fit.

(b) Using **3**

Taking two points on the line (1, 1.2) and (4, 1.5)

$$m = a = \text{gradient} = \frac{1.5 - 1.2}{4 - 1} = \frac{0.3}{3} = 0.1$$

and y intercept

$$c = b = 1.1$$

So $\quad s = 0.1\,t^2 + 1.1$

Revision exercise 11

1 This sketch shows part of the graph $y = pq^x$.
Find p and q and state the formula.

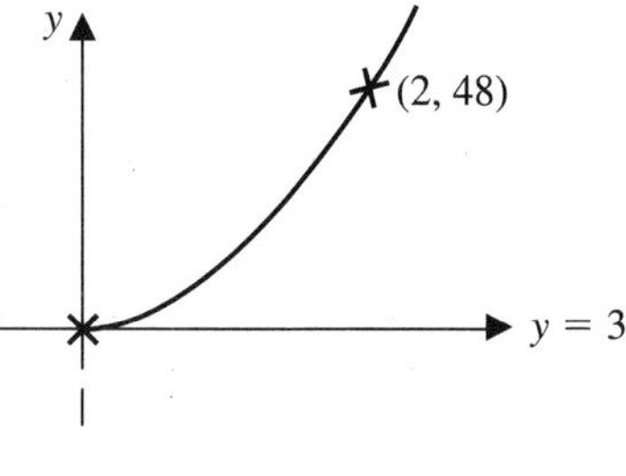

2 The sketch shows part of the graph $y = pq^x$.
Find p and q and state the formula.

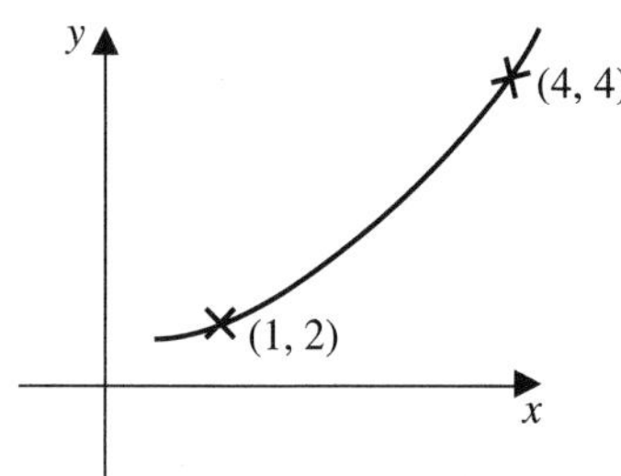

3 The value of a motorcycle decreases as shown in the table.

Years old (y)	0	1	2	3	4	5	6
Value (v)	5000	3000	1800	1080	648	389	233

(a) Draw a graph to confirm the relationship $v = pq^y$
(b) Use your graph to find p and q.

4

x	3	5	6	9	10
y	7	13	15	23	26

The table shows corresponding values of x and y.
The relationship between y and x is thought to be of the form $y = ax + b$.
(a) Confirm the relationship by drawing a suitable graph.
(b) Use your graph to estimate the values of a and b.

5

x	1	2	3	4	5	6
y	40	65	100	145	200	265

The data is thought to be approximately equal to the relationship $y = ax^2 + b$.
(a) Confirm the relationship by drawing a suitable graph.
(b) Use your graph to estimate the values of a and b.

6

x	1	2	3	4	5	6
y	3.7	12.4	26.1	44.8	68.5	97.2

The data is thought to be approximately equal to $y = ax^2 + bx$
(a) Draw a suitable graph to confirm the relationship.
(b) Use your graph to estimate the values of a and b.

7 A ball is dropped from a window. The time t seconds taken for the ball to fall a distance d feet is measured and recorded in the table below:

d	5	8	15	18	20	25
t	0.56	0.71	0.97	1.06	1.12	1.25
t^2						

(a) (i) Copy the table and complete the t^2 row.
(ii) Draw the graph of d against t^2 for $0 \leqslant d \leqslant 30$ and $0 \leqslant t^2 \leqslant 1.6$.
Explain how the graph indicates that $d = kt^2$ where k is a constant.

(b) Estimate the value of k to the nearest whole number.

[L, part]

Test yourself

What to review

1 The sketch shows part of the graph $y = pq^x$
Find the values of p and q.

If your answer is incorrect:

Review Higher book Unit 30, page 566, Example 8.

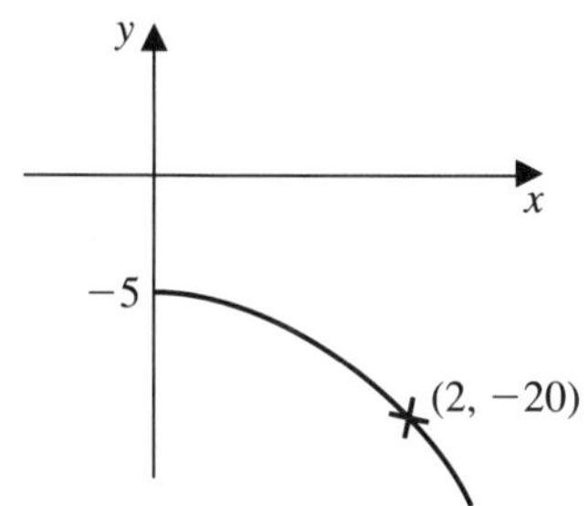

2

x	1	2	3	4	5
y	−0.4	4.4	12.4	23.6	38

The relationship between x and y is $y = ax^2 + b$
Find a and b.

Review Higher book Unit 30, page 563, Example 6.

3

x	3	4	5	6	7
y	10.2	15.6	22	29.4	37.8

The relationship between x and y is $y = ax^2 + bx$
Find a and b.

Review Higher book Unit 30, page 564, Example 7.

Answers to Test yourself

1 $p = -5, q = 2$ **2** $a = 1.6, b = -2$ **3** $a = 0.5, b = 1.9$

12 Pythagoras and trigonometry

Pythagoras' theorem is used to find the third side of a right-angled triangle when the lengths of the other two sides are known. Trigonometry is used to find the length of a side or the size of an angle in a right-angled triangle.

Key points to remember

1 For any right-angled triangle, the formula for Pythagoras' theorem is

$$a^2 + b^2 = c^2$$

where c is the hypotenuse.

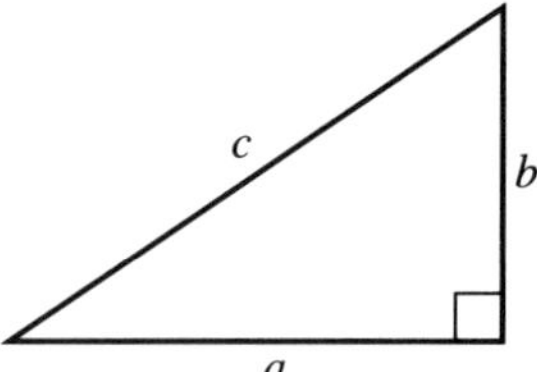

2 Pythagoras' theorem can be applied to problems set in three dimensions.
Always make a sketch of the triangle you need to use to answer the question.

3 The three trigonometric ratios are:

$$\sin\theta = \frac{\text{opp}}{\text{hyp}}$$

$$\cos\theta = \frac{\text{adj}}{\text{hyp}}$$

$$\tan\theta = \frac{\text{opp}}{\text{adj}}$$

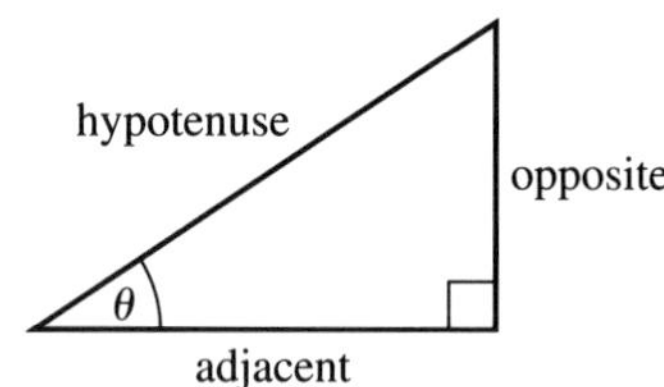

4 Trigonometry problems can be set in three dimensions.

5 Bearings are angles measured clockwise from North and expressed in three digits.

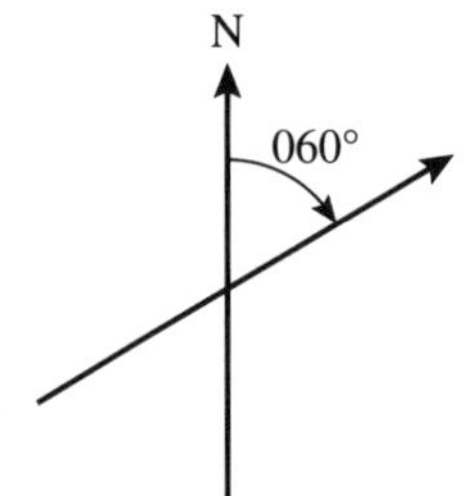

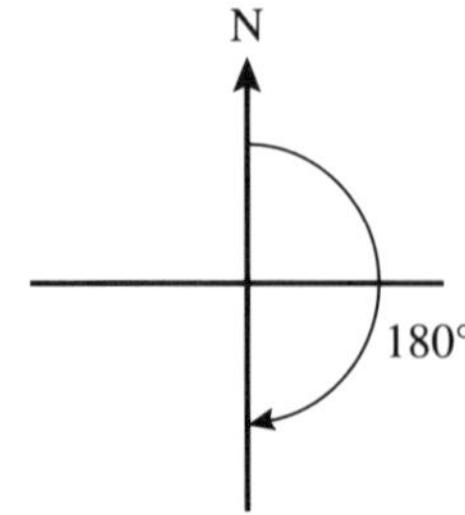

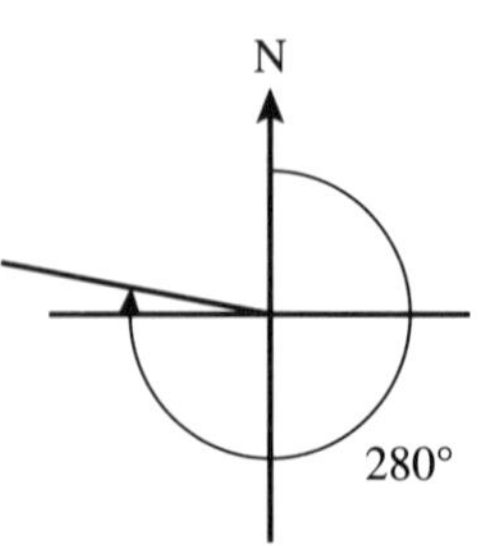

6 Angles of elevation and depression are measured from the horizontal.

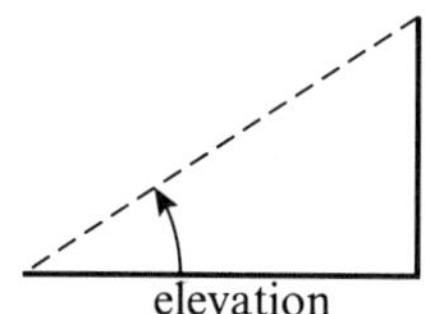

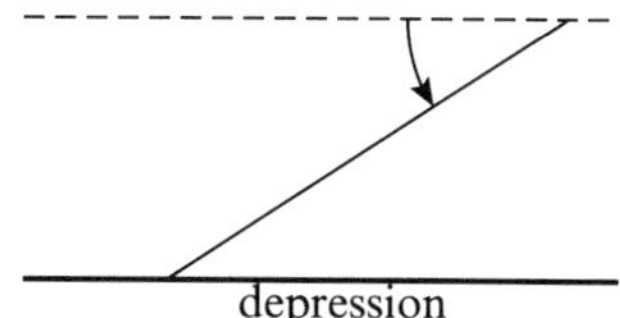

Example 1

$VABC$ is a tetrahedron.
The base ABC is a triangle.
The angle $ABC = 90°$
The vertex V is vertically above B

$AB = 7\,\text{cm}$ $\quad BC = 24\,\text{cm}$ $\quad VA = 18\,\text{cm}$

(a) Calculate the lengths of
  (i) AC (ii) VB

(b) Calculate the angles
  (i) ACB (ii) BAV

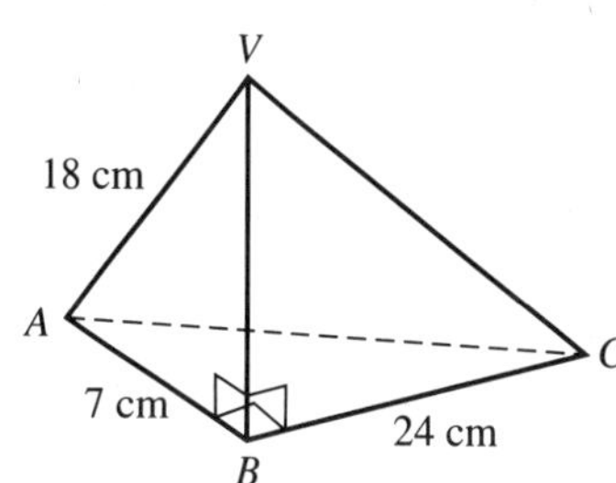

Answer

(a) (i) Using **1** and **2**
look at the base ABC.

$$AC^2 = AB^2 + BC^2$$
$$= 7^2 + 24^2$$
$$= 49 + 576$$
$$= 625$$

So $$AC = \sqrt{625}$$
$$= 25\,\text{cm}$$

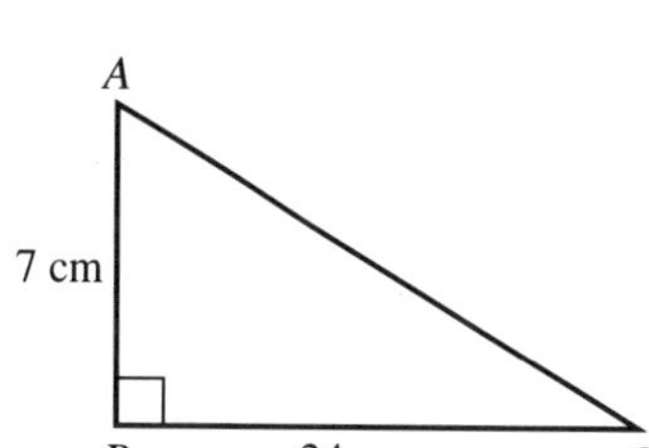

(ii) Using **1** and **2**
look at the plane face VBA.

$$VA^2 = AB^2 + VB^2$$
$$18^2 = 7^2 + VB^2$$
$$324 = 49 + VB^2$$
$$324 - 49 = VB^2$$

So $$VB^2 = 275$$
$$VB = \sqrt{275}$$
$$= 16.58\,\text{cm (2 d.p.)}$$

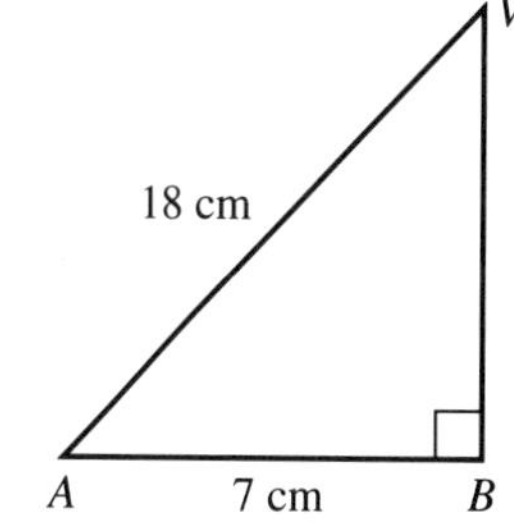

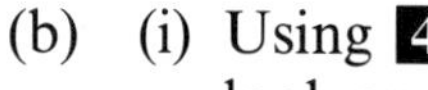
(b) (i) Using **4**
look again at the base ABC.
Using **3**

$$\tan ACB = \frac{7}{24}$$
$$\tan ACB = 0.291\,66$$
$$ACB = 16.26°$$

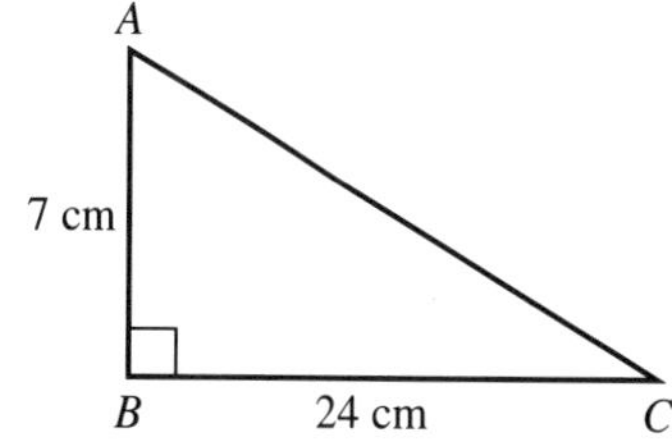

(b) (ii) Using **4**
look again at the face VBA
Using **3**

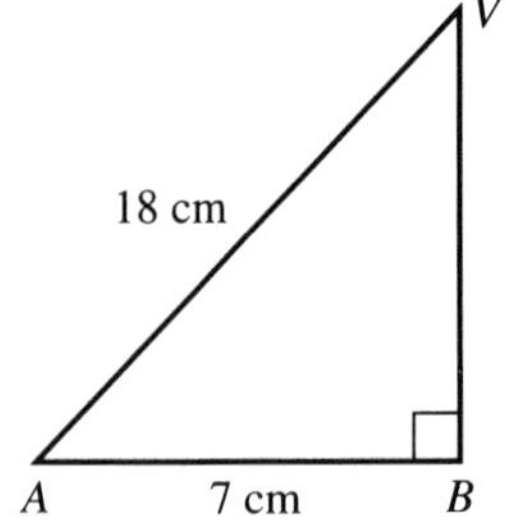

$$\cos BAV = \frac{7}{18}$$
$$= 0.3888\ldots$$
$$\text{angle } BAV = 67.11^\circ$$

Worked examination question [L]

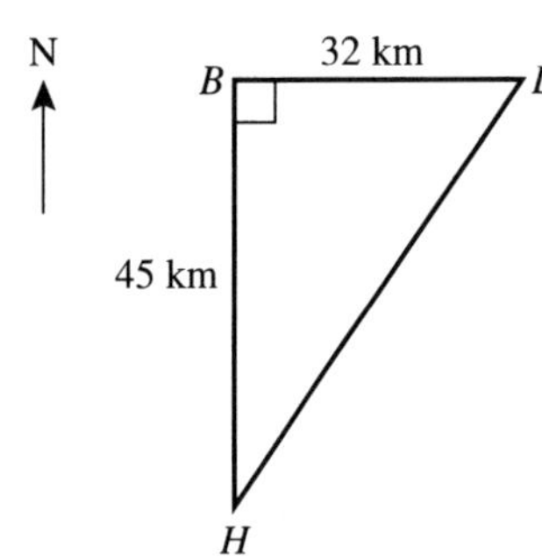

The diagram shows the path taken by a yacht.
The yacht leaves a harbour H.
It travels 45 km due North to a marker buoy B.
At B the yacht turns and travels a further 32 km due East to a lighthouse L.
At L the yacht turns again and travels in a straight line back to the harbour H.

(a) Calculate the total distance travelled by the yacht.
(b) Calculate the bearing of L from H.

On its return journey from L to H the yacht passes through a point P.
This point P is the point on the line LH such that the yacht is at its closest point, on the return journey, to the marker buoy B.

(c) Calculate the distance from P to B.
(d) Calculate the bearing of P from B.

Answer

(a) Using **1** calculate LH

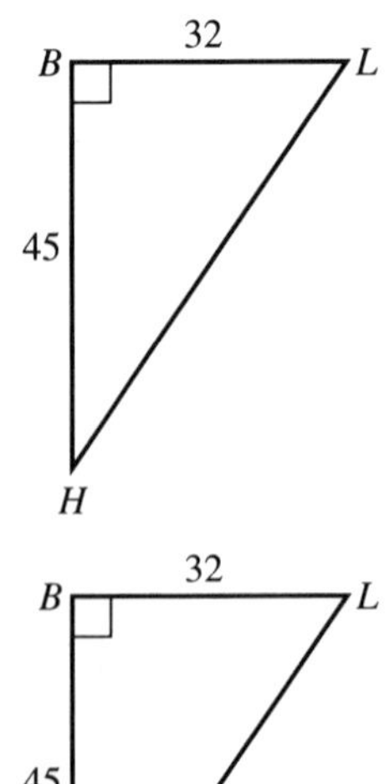

$$LH^2 = HB^2 + BL^2$$
$$= 45^2 + 32^2$$
$$= 2025 + 1024$$
$$= 3049$$
$$LH = 55.22\text{ km}$$

So the total distance travelled by the yacht is
$$45 + 32 + 55.22 = 132.22\text{ km}$$

(b) Using **3** and **5**
find the angle x

$$\tan x = \frac{32}{45} = 0.471\,11\ldots$$
$$x = 35.4^\circ$$

So the bearing of L from H is 035° to the nearest degree.

(c) P must be on LH. For PB to be the minimum distance, BP must be perpendicular to LH.

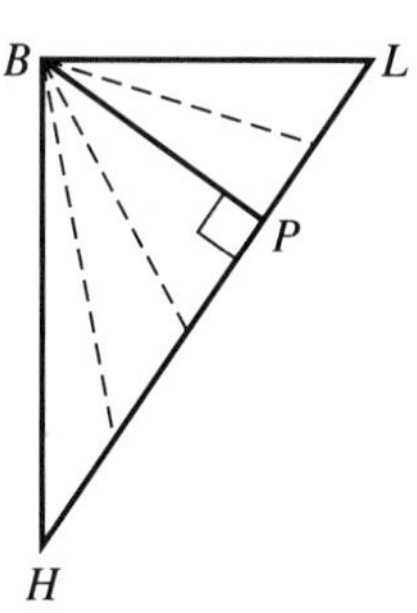

Using **3**

$$\sin x = \frac{BP}{BH}$$

$$\sin 35.4 = \frac{BP}{45}$$

So $$BP = 45 \times \sin 35.4$$
$$= 45 \times 0.57928$$
$$= 26.07\,\text{km}$$

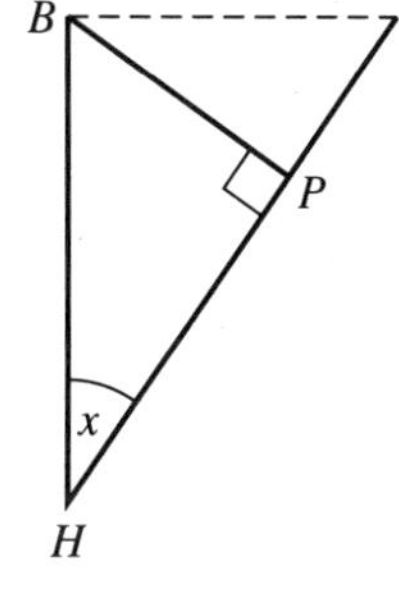

(d) Find the angle NBP.

$$\text{Angle } NBP = x + 90°$$
$$= 35.4° + 90°$$
$$= 125.4°$$

The bearing of P from B is 125° to the nearest degree.

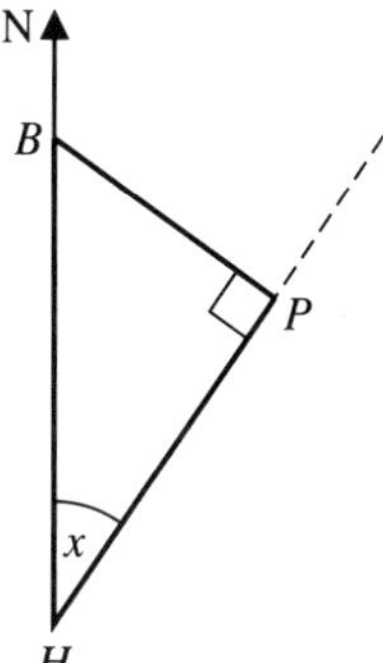

Example 2

In the triangle ABC, $AC = 15\,\text{cm}$, angle $ABC = 62°$ and angle $BAC = 90°$

Calculate the length of BC.

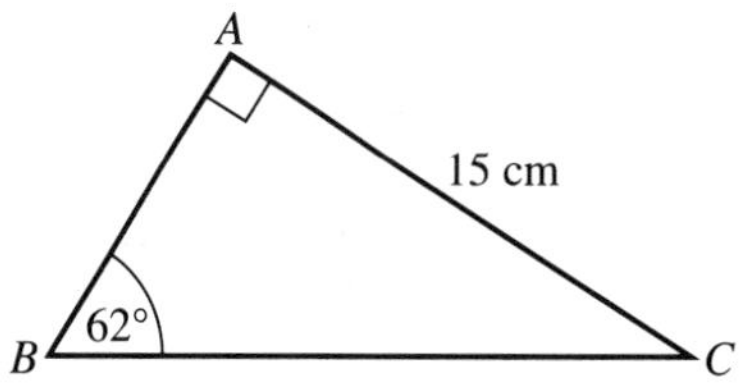

Answer

Using **3**

$$\frac{15}{BC} = \sin 62°$$

So $$\frac{15}{\sin 62°} = BC$$

So $$BC = 16.99\,\text{cm}.$$

Revision exercise 12

1 The diagram shows a triangle PQR

$PQ = 6\,\text{cm} \quad RQ = 18\,\text{cm}$

Calculate

(a) the perimeter of the triangle PQR
(b) the area of the triangle PQR
(c) the angle marked. [L]

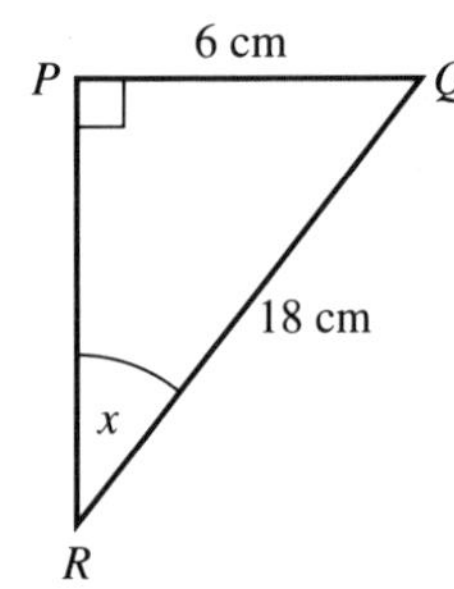

2 The diagram shows the path taken by a ship.
The ship leaves a port P.
It sails 120 km due North to a lighthouse L.
At L the ship turns due West and travels a further 50 km due West to a marker buoy B.

At B the ship turns again and travels back to P in a straight line.

Calculate

(a) the total distance travelled by the ship.
(b) the bearing of B from P.
(c) the shortest distance between the ship and L on the ship's return journey from B to P.

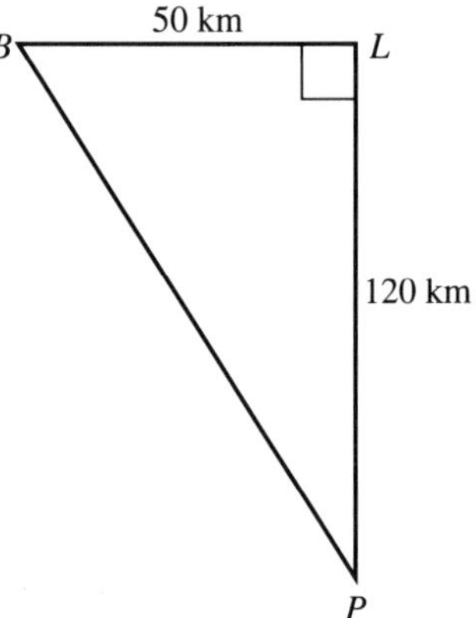

Diagram not accurately drawn

3 The diagram represents a cuboid $ABCDEFGH$.

$AB = 6\,\text{cm} \qquad BC = 15\,\text{cm} \qquad CD = 5\,\text{cm}$

Calculate

(a) the length of BG.
(b) the length of BE.
(c) the angle between BE and BG.

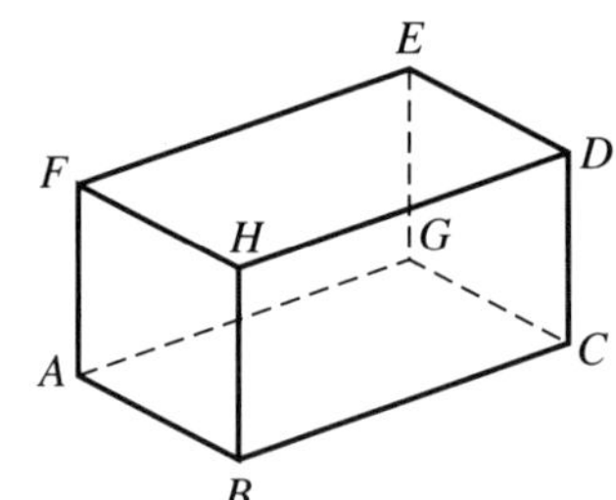

4

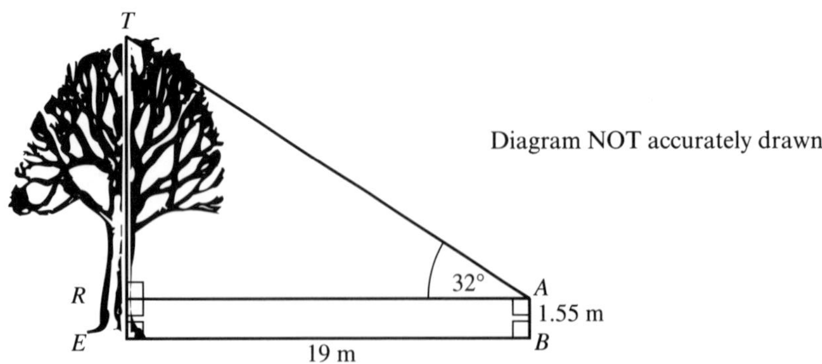

Abbi is standing on level ground, at B, a distance of 19 metres away from the foot E of a tree TE.

She measures the angle of elevation of the top of the tree at a height of 1.55 metres above the ground as 32°.
Calculate the height TE of the tree. Give your answer correct to 3 significant figures. [L]

5 The diagram shows a wedge $ABCDEF$.
The horizontal base $BCDE$ is a rectangle
$BC = 15\,\text{cm} \qquad CD = 24\,\text{cm}$
The face $ABEF$ is in the vertical plane.
Angle ABC = Angle $FED = 90°$
$AC = FD = 17\,\text{cm}$
Calculate
(a) the length of AB
(b) the length of CE
(c) the angle ACB
(d) the angle FCE

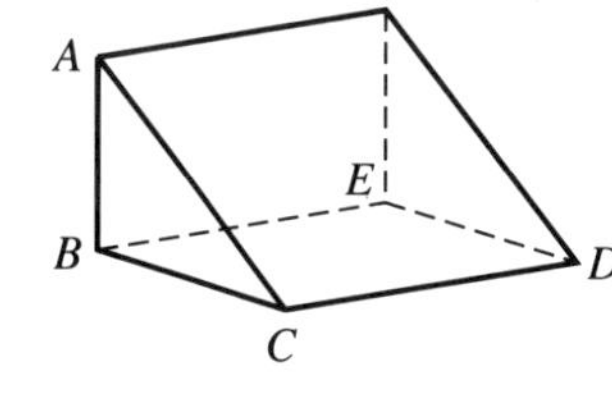

6 $VABCD$ is a pyramid.
The base $ABCD$ is a square.
The vertex V is vertically above point M, the centre of the base.
$VB = 25\,\text{cm} \qquad AB = 12\,\text{cm}$
Calculate
(a) the length of AC
(b) the length of BM
(c) the angle VBM.

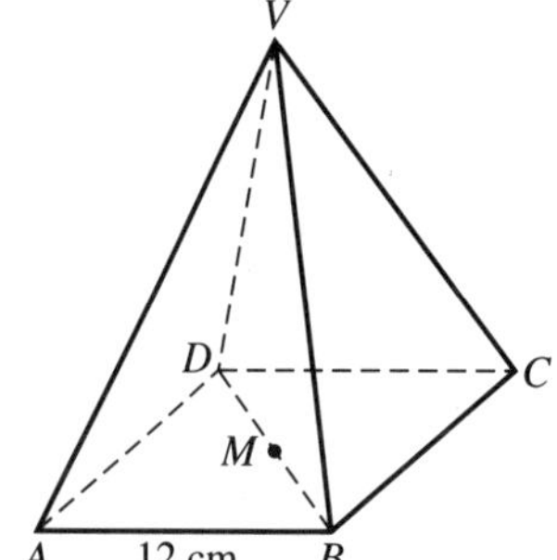

7 $SPQR$ is a tetrahedron.
The base PQR is a triangle, with angle $PQR = 90°$
The vertex S is vertically above Q.
$SR = 41\,\text{cm} \qquad SQ = 40\,\text{cm} \qquad PQ = 12\,\text{cm}$

Calculate
(a) the angle QRS
(b) the length of QR
(c) the length of PR
(d) the angle SPQ.

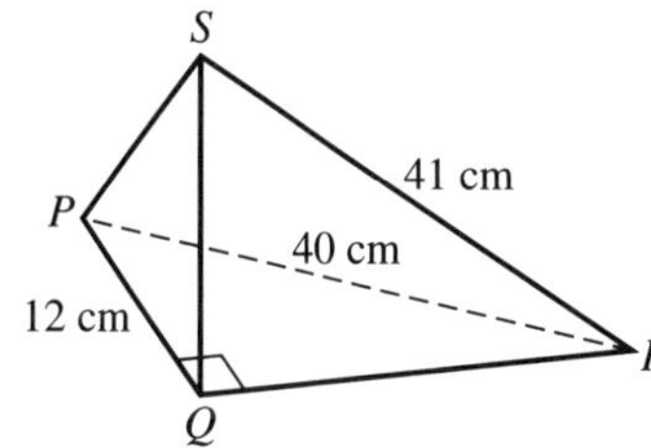

8 ABC is a triangle with angle $ABC = 90°$, angle $BCA = 71°$ and the length of BC is 8 cm.

Work out the length of AC.

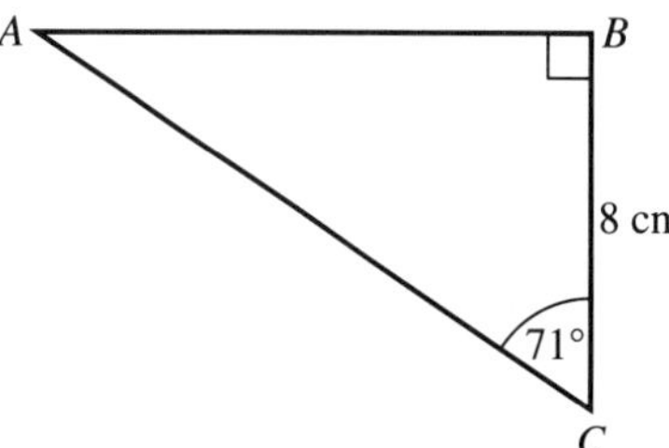

9 Right angled triangles can have sides with lengths which are a rational or irrational number of units.
Give an example of a right angled triangle to fit each description below.
(i) All sides are rational
(ii) The hypotenuse is rational and the other two sides are irrational.
(iii) The hypotenuse is irrational and the other two sides are rational.
(iv) The hypotenuse and one of the other two sides are rational and the remaining side is irrational. [L]

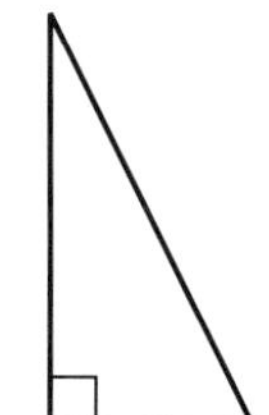

Test yourself

What to review

1 The diagram shows the path taken by a man on a walk.
The man leaves his home H and walks 4.3 km due North to a stile S.
At S he turns due West and walks a further 2.2 km to a crossroads C.
At C he turns again and walks back to his home in a straight line.

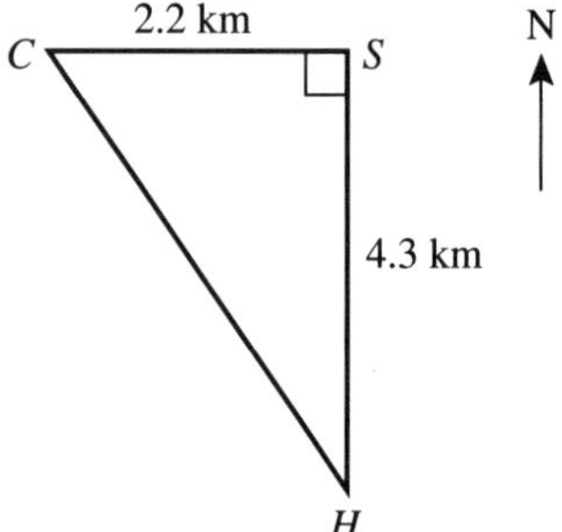

If your answer is incorrect:

(a) Calculate the total distance walked by the man.
Give your answer in kilometres, correct to 2 d.p.

Review Higher book Unit 8, page 162, Example 2.

(b) Calculate the bearing of C from H.
Give your answer correct to the nearest degree.

Review Higher book Unit 13, page 234, Example 4.

---

2 $ABCDEFGH$ is a cuboid.
$AB = 5\,\text{cm}$ $BC = 12\,\text{cm}$ $AF = 8\,\text{cm}$

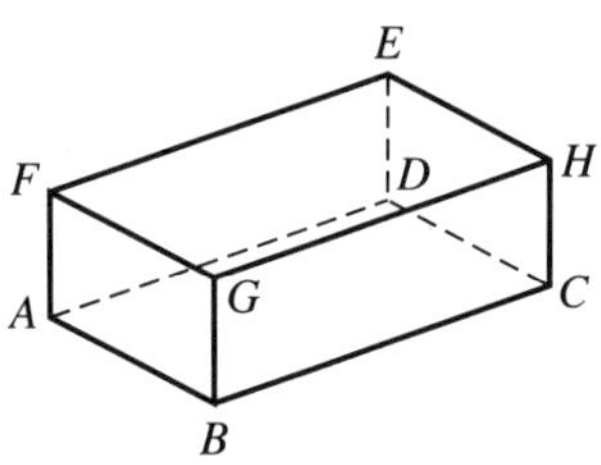

(a) Calculate the length of FB.
Give your answer in cm correct to 2 d.p.

Review Higher book Unit 8, page 168, Example 8.

(b) Calculate the length of the diagonal BE.
Give your answer in cm correct to 2 d.p.

Review Higher book Unit 8, page 168, Example 8.

(c) Calculate the value of the angle FBA.
Give your answer correct to the nearest degree.

Review Higher book Unit 22, page 414, Example 9.

(d) Calculate the value of the angle EBF.
Give your answer correct to the nearest degree.

Review Higher book Unit 22, page 414, Example 9.

Answers to Test yourself

1 **(a)** 11.33 km **(b)** 333° **2** **(a)** 9.43 cm **(b)** 15.26 cm **(c)** 58° **(d)** 52°

13 Similarity and enlargement

Two shapes are similar when they look the same but one is bigger than the other.

Key points to remember

1 Shapes are similar if one shape is an enlargement of the other.

2 When two shapes are similar the corresponding sides are in proportion and corresponding angles are equal.

3 The scale factor of enlargement is the ratio:

$$\frac{\text{length of a side on one shape}}{\text{length of corresponding side on the other shape}}$$

4 An enlargement can have a positive, negative or fractional scale factor.
The image will be reduced if the scale factor is smaller than 1.
A negative scale factor indicates that the measuring from the centre of enlargement must be in the opposite direction.
To describe an enlargement, state the centre and the scale factor.

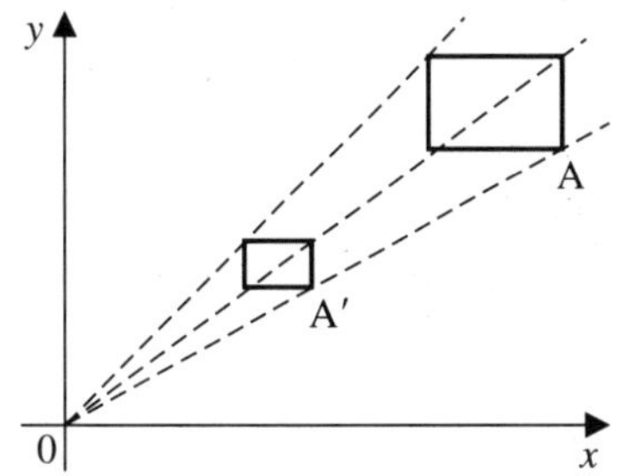

A' is an enlargement of A, scale factor $\frac{1}{2}$, centre the origin.

5 If the scale factor is ± 1, the two shapes are identical and are said to be congruent.

6 When the scale factor of the length of two similar shapes is k, then the scale factor of the areas of the two shapes is k^2 (and the scale factor of volumes is k^3).

Example 1

The vertices of triangle ABC are at the points

$A\ (2, 2)$ $B\ (4, 2)$ $C\ (2, 6)$

The image of ABC after an enlargement scale factor $-1\frac{1}{2}$ centre $(0, 0)$ is $A'B'C'$.

Work out the coordinates of $A'B'C'$.

Answer

Image after an enlargement centre (0, 0) scale factor $-1\frac{1}{2}$.
Using **4** the 'negative' enlargement goes in the 'opposite' direction.

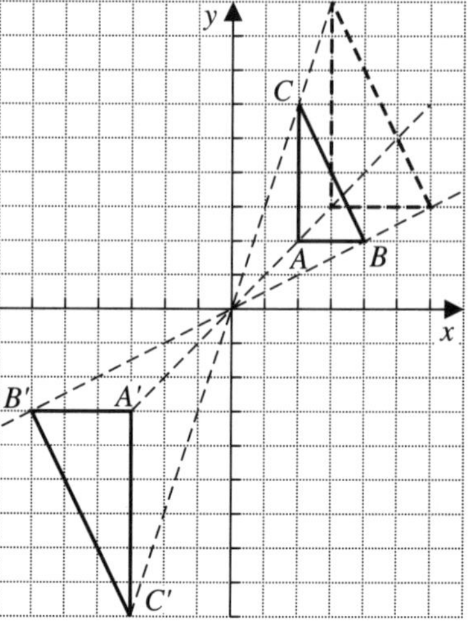

To find the coordinates of the image when the centre is the origin, multiply the coordinates by the scale factor, so

$A = (2, 2)$ becomes $A' = (2 \times -1\frac{1}{2}, 2 \times -1\frac{1}{2}) = (-3, -3)$.

$B = (4, 2)$ becomes $B' = (4 \times -1\frac{1}{2}, 2 \times -1\frac{1}{2}) = (-6, -3)$.

$C = (2, 6)$ becomes $C' = (2 \times -1\frac{1}{2}, 6 \times -1\frac{1}{2}) = (-3, -9)$.

So A' is $(-3, -3)$, B' is $(-6, -3)$, C' is $(-3, -9)$

Worked examination question [L]

In the diagram $FG = 5.6$ metres, $EH = 3.5$ metres and $DH = 15$ metres. EH is parallel to FG.
FED and DHG are straight lines.

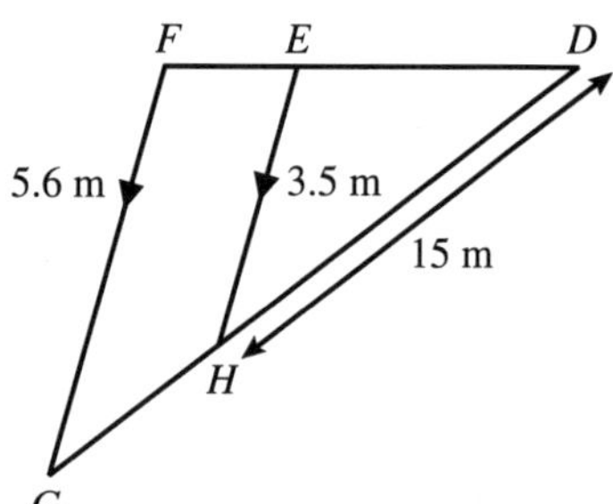

Calculate
(a) the length of DG.
(b) the ratio of the areas of triangles DEH and DFG.

Answer

(a) For triangles DEH and DFG
$\hat{D}$ is common to both.
$\hat{E} = \hat{F}$; $\hat{H} = \hat{G}$ (parallel lines)
So using **2** these two triangles are similar.
Using **3** the scale factor of the enlargement is

$$\frac{FG}{EH} = \frac{5.6}{3.5} = 1.6$$

So, using **3** again

$$\frac{DG}{DH} = \text{scale factor} = 1.6$$

$$\frac{DG}{15} = 1.6$$

$$DG = 15 \times 1.6 = 24\,\text{cm}$$

(b) Using **6** ratio of lengths $= 1 : 1.6$
so ratio of areas $= 1 : 1.6^2$
$= 1 : 2.56$
$= 25 : 64$

Revision exercise 13

1 Zoe wanted to find the height of a tower in the park.
She placed a 1.6 m pole upright in the shadow of the tower. The end of the shadow of the pole was in the same place as the end of the shadow of the tower.
Her brother Andrew then took measurements. The measurements are shown in the diagram.

Use the measurements to calculate the height, h metres, of the tower. [L]

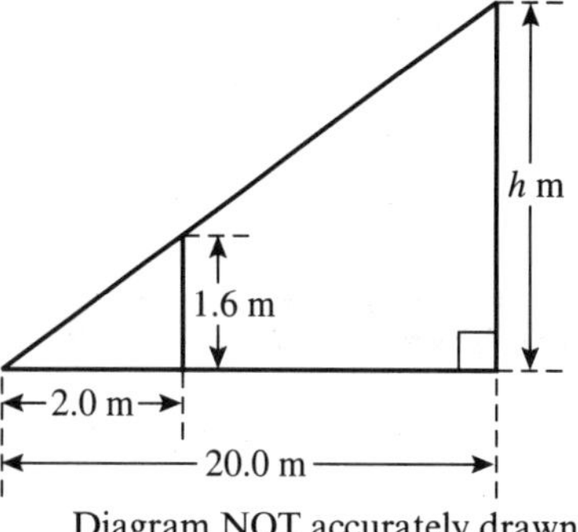

Diagram NOT accurately drawn

2 In the diagram angle ABC = angle CDE = angle $CEF = 65°$
and length $AB = 3\,\text{cm}$
length $AC = 4\,\text{cm}$
length $CE = 7\,\text{cm}$

(a) Calculate the length DE.
(b) Write down two triangles which are similar to triangle ABC. [L]

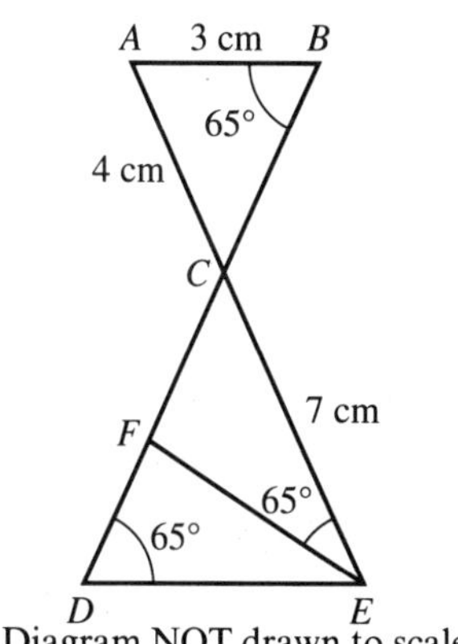

Diagram NOT drawn to scale

3 Triangle PQR has its vertices at

$P(4, 7)$ $Q(7, 7)$ $R(7, 13)$

PQR is enlarged by a scale factor of $-\frac{1}{3}$ centre $(1, 1)$ to form $P'Q'R'$.

Find the coordinates of P', Q' and R'.

4 AC is parallel to XY.

$AC = 7\,\text{cm}$, $XY = 4\,\text{cm}$, $AB = 12\,\text{cm}$

(a) Explain why the triangles ABC and XBY are similar.
(b) Calculate the length of XB.
(c) Calculate the ratio:

$$\frac{\text{area } ABC}{\text{area } XBY}$$ [L]

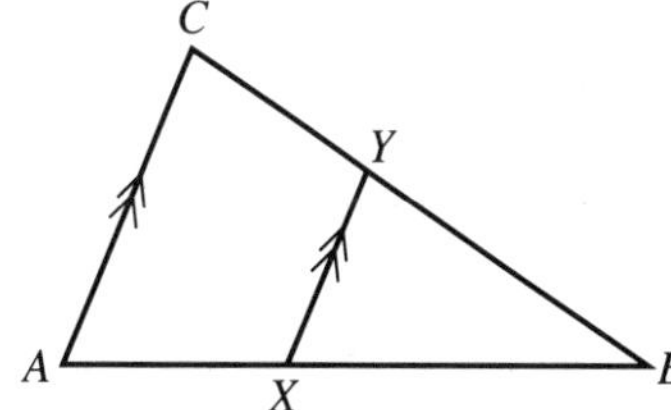

5 A shape S is transformed by an enlargement scale factor $-k$, centre P to form an image S'.

S' is then transformed by a scale factor $\frac{1}{k}$, centre Q to form a second image S''.

Explain whether or not S and S'' are congruent.

6 ABC is a triangle with $CAB = 90°$.
AP is perpendicular to BC.
P lies on BC.

$AB = 12\,\text{cm}, \qquad AC = 5\,\text{cm}$

Calculate the length of AP, giving your reasons.

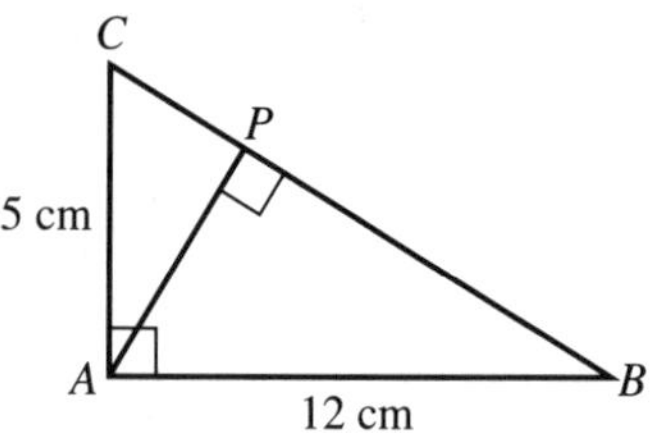

Test yourself | What to review

1 PQ is parallel to ST.
$PQ = 3\,\text{cm}$,
$TS = 8\,\text{cm}$,
$RT = 12\,\text{cm}$

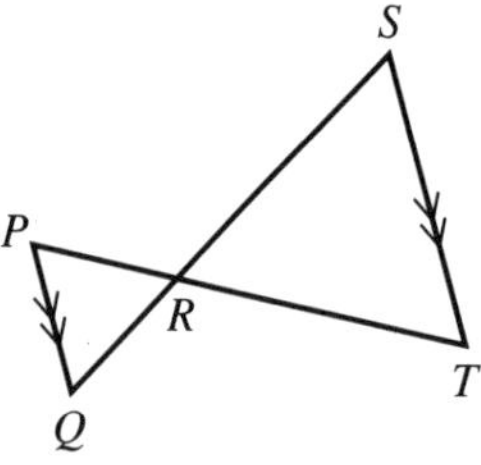

If your answer is incorrect:

(a) Explain why triangles PQR and TSR are similar. — *Review Higher book Unit 2, page 47, Section 3.9.*

(b) Calculate the length of PR. — *Review Higher book Unit 3, page 49, Example 7.*

(c) Calculate the ratio

$$\frac{\text{area } PQR}{\text{area } TSR}$$

— *Review Higher book Unit 19, page 349, Section 19.3.*

---

2 Triangle $OA'B'$ is formed by enlarging triangle OAB, centre O.

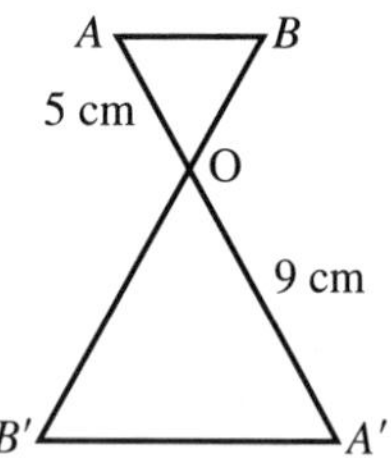

(a) Comment on the correctness of the statement
'The scale factor of the enlargement is 1.8' — *Review Higher book Unit 6, pages 127–8.*

(b) Copy the diagram and show clearly where a line segment XY should be drawn so that triangle OAB and OXY are congruent. — *Review Higher book Unit 3, page 44, Section 3.8.*

Answers to Test yourself

1 (a) $\widehat{R}$ is common, $\widehat{Q} = \widehat{S}$ $\widehat{P} = \widehat{T}$ **(b)** $4\frac{1}{2}$ cm **(c)** $\frac{9}{64}$

2 (a) The scale factor should be −1.8. **(b)**

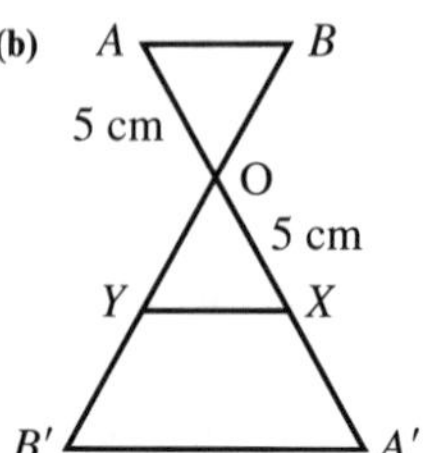

14 Advanced trigonometry

Key points to remember

1 Area of triangle $= \frac{1}{2}ab\sin C$

2 The Sine Rule

$$\frac{a}{\sin A} = \frac{b}{\sin B} = \frac{c}{\sin C}$$

and

$$\frac{\sin A}{a} = \frac{\sin B}{b} = \frac{\sin C}{c}$$

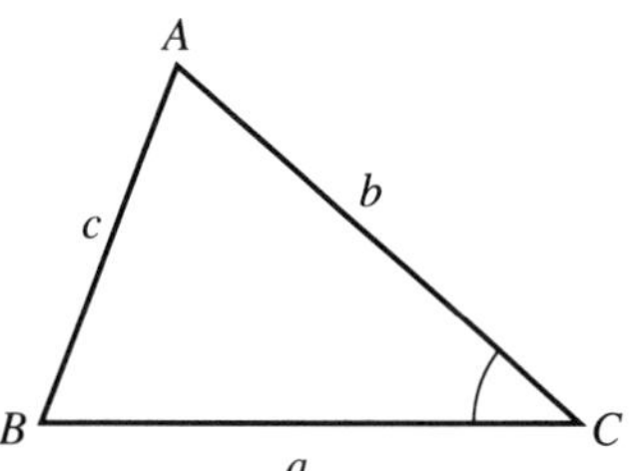

3 The Cosine Rule

$$c^2 = a^2 + b^2 - 2ab\cos C$$

and

$$\cos C = \frac{a^2 + b^2 - c^2}{2ab}$$

Worked examination question [L]

A farmer fences off a triangular field PQR.

$PQ = 64\,\text{m} \qquad PR = 43\,\text{m}$

Angle $QPR = 72°$

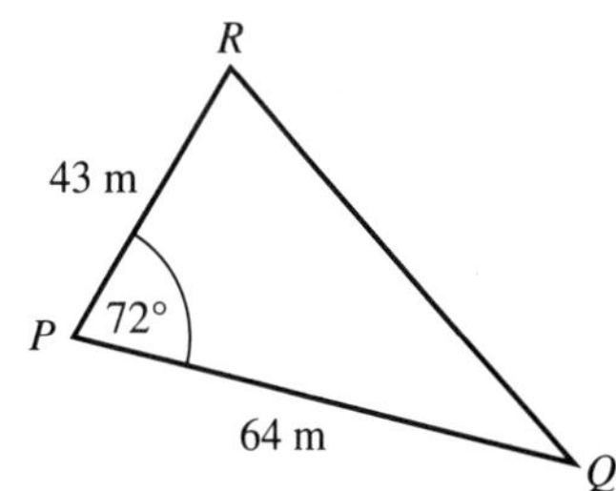

Calculate

(a) the area of the field

(b) the perimeter of the field

(c) the angle PQR.

Answer

(a) Using **1**

$$\text{Area} = \tfrac{1}{2} \times 64 \times 43 \times \sin 72° = 1308.65\,\text{m}^2$$

(b) Perimeter $= 64\,\text{m} + 43\,\text{m} + RQ$

Using **3**

$$RQ^2 = 64^2 + 43^2 - 2 \times 64 \times 43 \times \cos 72°$$
$$= 4096 + 1849 - 1700.83$$
$$= 5945 - 1700.83 = 4244.17$$
$$RQ = \sqrt{4244.17} = 65.15\,\text{m}$$

So perimeter $= 64 + 43 + 65.15 = 172.15\,\text{m}$

(c) Using **2**

$$\frac{\sin PQR}{43} = \frac{\sin 72^\circ}{65.15}$$

$$\sin PQR = \frac{43 \times \sin 72^\circ}{65.15}$$

$$= 0.6277$$

$$\text{Angle } PQR = 38.88^\circ$$

Example 1

In the triangle ABC opposite, work out the size of the angle marked θ.

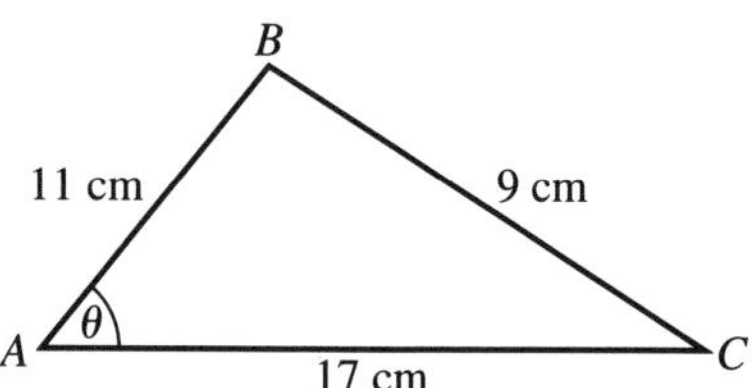

Answer

Using **3**

$$\cos\theta = \frac{17^2 + 11^2 - 9^2}{2 \times 17 \times 11}$$

$$\cos\theta = \frac{329}{374}$$

so $\theta = 28.4^\circ$ (1 d.p.)

Revision exercise 14

1 In each of these triangles the lengths are in centimetres.
For each triangle, calculate the area and the length of the side marked x.

(a)

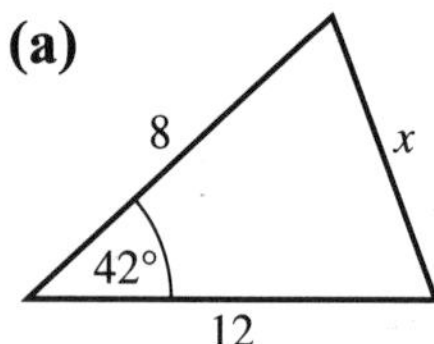

(b)

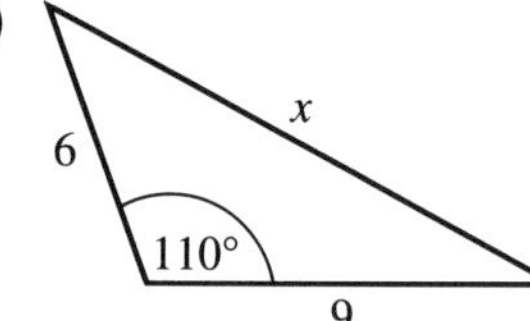

2 Two ships leave port C.

Ship P travels on a bearing of 060° for 13 km to A.
Ship Q travels on a bearing of 315° for 17 km to B.
Calculate the bearing of B from A.

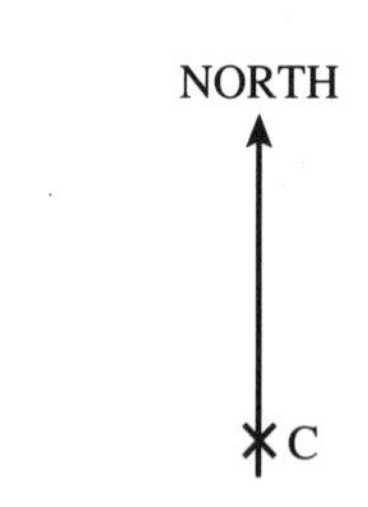

3 Speedboats race around the triangular circuit A to B to C to A as shown in the diagram.

$AB = 5.0$ km, $BC = 7.0$ km and angle $BAC = 60^\circ$
$AC = x$ km

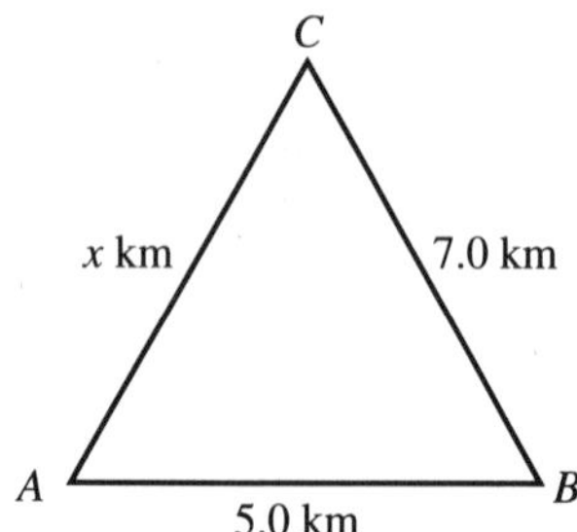

(a) Using the Cosine Rule, show that

$$x^2 - 5x - 24 = 0$$

The speedboats are taking part in a 100 km race.

(b) By calculating the value of x, work out how many times around the circuit, ABC, the speedboats should travel. [L]

4

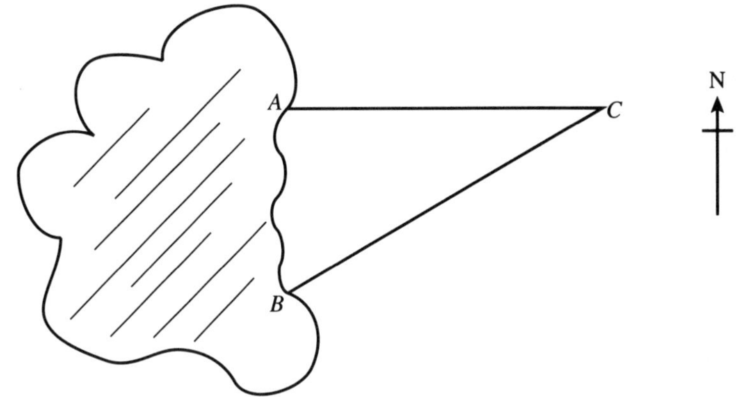

On this island, Port A is due North of Port B.
A ship leaves Port B and travels on a bearing of 060° for 50 km.
The ship is now due East of A at point C.
(a) Calculate the distance from Port A to point C.

At the same time as the first ship leaves Port B, another ship leaves port A on a bearing of 145°. Both ships travel at constant speeds and meet after 2 hours.
(b) Calculate the speed of each ship. [L]

5 In the diagram, XY represents a vertical tower on level ground.
A and B are points due West of Y.
The distance AB is 30 metres.

The angle of elevation of X from A is 30°.
The angle of elevation of X from B is 50°.

Calculate the height, in metres, of the tower XY.
Give your answer correct to 1 decimal place. [L]

Diagram NOT accurately drawn

6 Calculate the angle marked x.

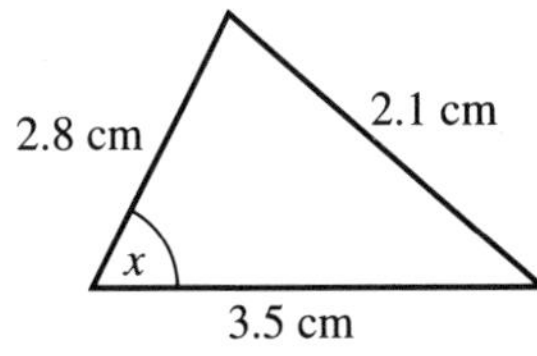

7

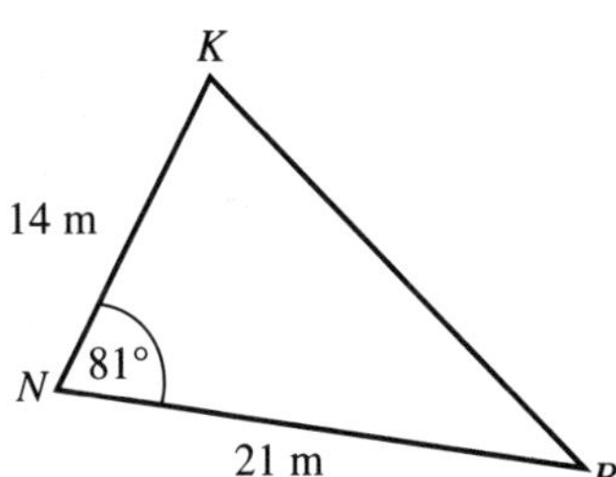

(a) Calculate the length KB.
(b) Calculate the size of the angle NKB [L]

8 In a triangle PQR

$$PQ = 12\,\text{cm},\ PR = 8\,\text{cm and the area of } PQR = 38\,\text{cm}^2.$$

(a) Calculate the two possible values for the angle QPR.
(b) In both cases calculate the length of QR.

9 A ship S, leaves a harbour H.
The ship travels 42 km due North until it reaches a marker buoy B.
At B the ship turns on a bearing of 073° and travels for a further 70 km until it reaches a lighthouse L.
At L the ship turns again and travels back to H in a straight line.
Calculate
(a) the total distance travelled by the ship.
(b) the bearing of L from H.
(c) the shortest distance between S and B on the ship's return journey from L to H.

10

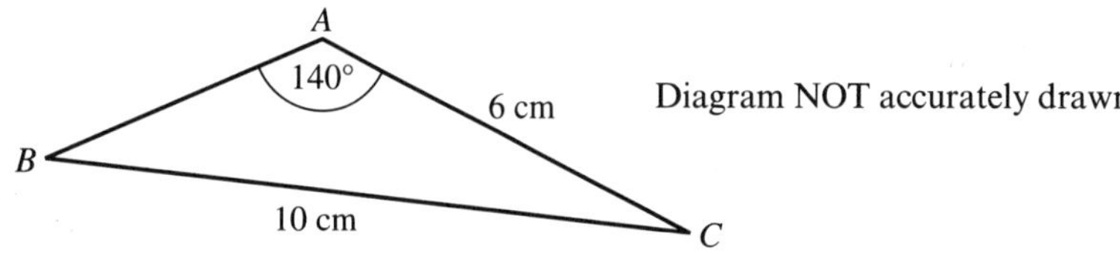

$AC = 6\,\text{cm}$, $BC = 10\,\text{cm}$, Angle $B\widehat{A}C = 140°$.
Calculate angle ACB. Give your answer to the nearest tenth of a degreee. [L]

Test yourself | What to review

1 The town of Lucea is 18 km due North of the town of Preble. The town of Manwell is 24 km from Preble on a bearing of 340° from Preble.
The towns are joined by three straight roads.

If your answer is incorrect:

(a) Calculate the distance from Lucea to Manwell.
Review Higher book Unit 22, page 411, Example 7.

(b) Calculate the area enclosed by the three roads.
Review Higher book Unit 22, page 403, Examples 1 and 2.

(c) Calculate the bearing of Lucea from Manwell.
Review Higher book Unit 22, page 407, Example 5.

Answers to Test yourself

1 **(a)** 9.39 km **(b)** 73.88 km^2 **(c)** 119°

15 Trigonometry: angles greater than 90°

Trigonometry can be extended to angles of all sizes.

Key points to remember

1 The graph of $\sin x$ is

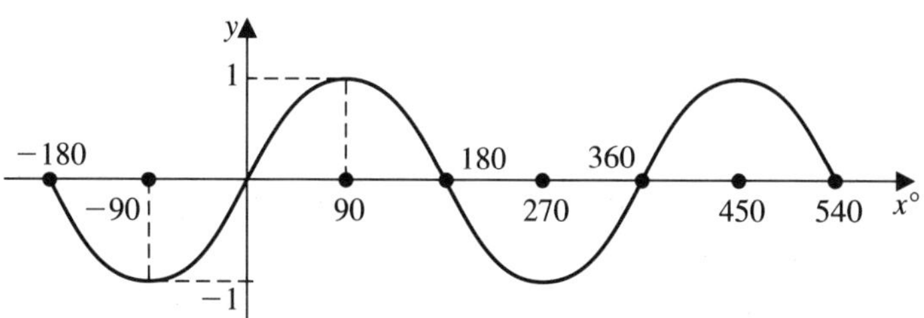

2 The graph of $\cos x$ is

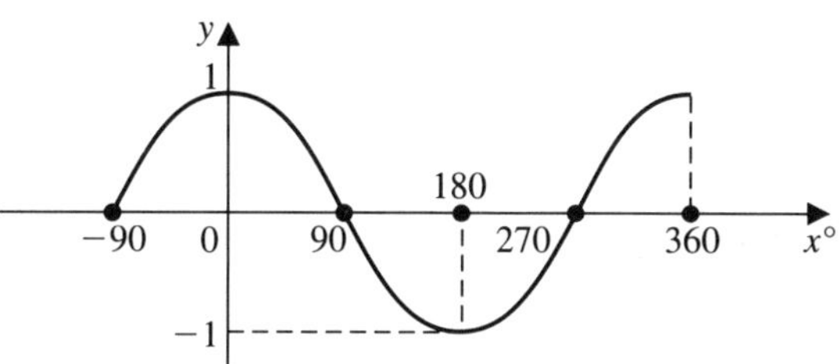

3 The graph of $\tan x$ is

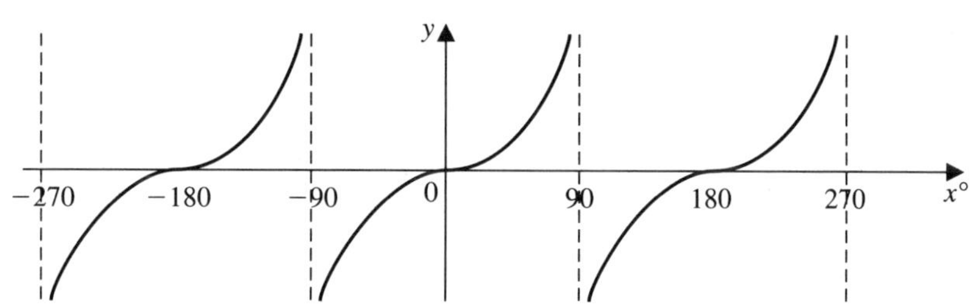

4 You need to be able to solve equations such as

$$\tan x = 2$$

for $0° \leqslant x \leqslant 360°$

Example 1

Find all solutions of the equation

$$3 \sin x° = 2$$

in the range $0° \leqslant x \leqslant 360°$

Answer

$$3 \sin x = 2$$

is the same as

$$\sin x = \tfrac{2}{3}$$

So, from the calculator, one solution is

$$x = 41.8° \text{ (to 1 d.p.)}$$

Using **1** the graph of $\sin x$ is

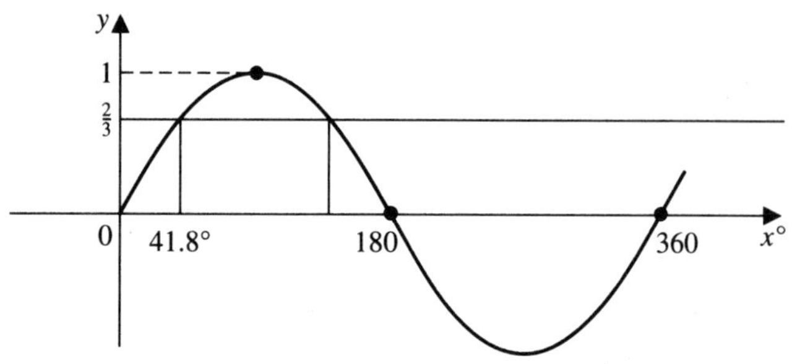

So in the range $0° \leqslant x \leqslant 360°$, the second solution to $\sin x = \frac{2}{3}$ is

$$x = 180 - 41.8 = 138.2°$$

The two solutions are

$$x = 41.8° \text{ and } x = 138.2°$$

(both correct to 1 d.p.)

Worked examination question [L]

Draw the graph of

$$y = 4 \cos x°$$

By drawing an appropriate straight line, find solutions of the equation

$$4 \cos x° = \frac{x°}{36} \text{ in the range } -180 \leqslant x \leqslant 180$$

Answer

Taking some values of x:

$x°$	$\cos x°$	$y = 4 \cos x°$
−180	−1	−4
−135	−0.707	−2.83
−90	0	0
−45	0.707	2.83
0	1	4
45	0.707	2.83
90	0	0
135	−0.707	−2.83
180	−1	−4

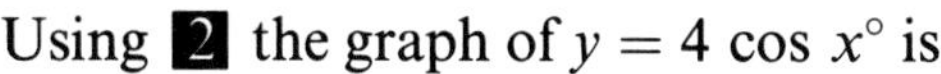

Using **2** the graph of $y = 4 \cos x°$ is

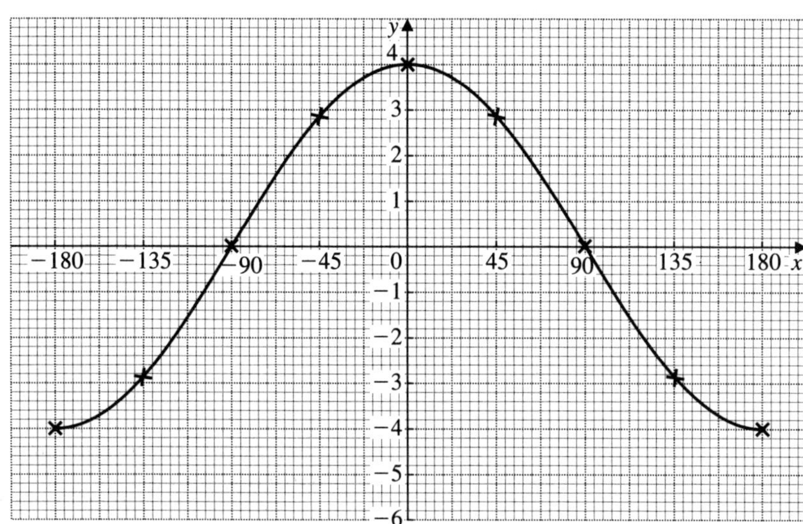

The solutions of

$$4 \cos x° = \frac{x°}{36}$$

occur at the points of intersection of

$$y = 4 \cos x° \text{ and } y = \frac{x°}{36}$$

On the graph draw

$$y = \frac{x°}{36}$$

which is a straight line passing through the points

$x = 0, \quad y = 0,$

$x = 180°, \ y = 5.$

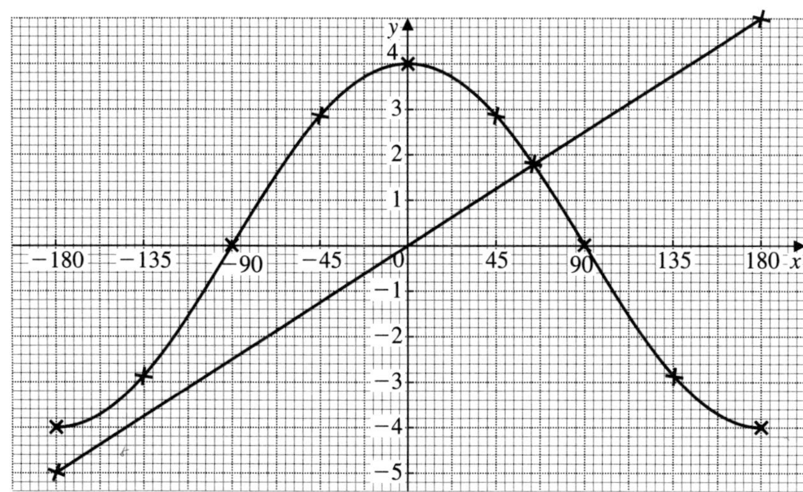

From the graph, the only solution is $x = 63.7°$.

Example 2

For all values of $x°$ in the range $0 \leqslant x < 360$, find the solutions of

$$\sin 3x° = \sin 60°$$

Answer

One solution is when

$$3x = 60° \text{ i.e. } x = 20°$$

Also $\sin 60° = 0.866$

So the solutions are when

$$\sin 3x = 0.866$$

Using **1** the graph of $\sin 3x$ is

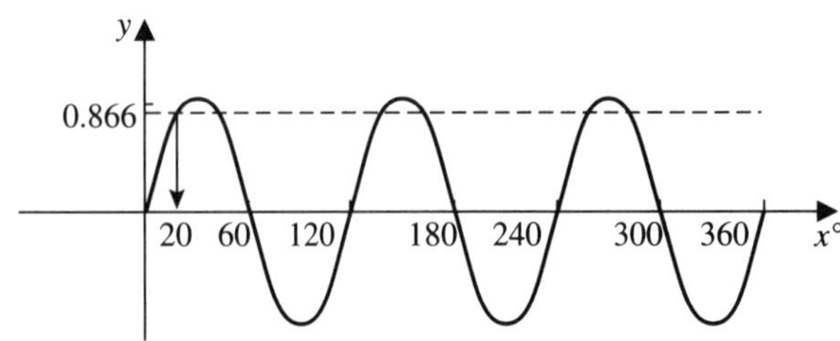

There is more information on sketching graphs in Unit 9.

From the graph, the other solutions are

$$x = 20°, 40°, 140°, 160°, 260°, 280°.$$

Revision exercise 15

1 Find two different values of x between 0 and 180 for which

$$\sin (2x)° = \sin 30°$$ [L]

2 Draw the graph of

$$y = \cos 2x°$$

for $0 \leqslant x \leqslant 180$.

3 Work out all the solutions of

$$\tan x° = 3$$

in the range $0 \leqslant x \leqslant 180$.

4 Work out all the solutions of

$$2 \cos x° = 1$$

in the range $-360° \leqslant x \leqslant 360$.

5 Find the solutions of

$$\cos (2x)° = \cos 60°$$

in the range $-180 \leqslant x \leqslant 180$.

6 Sketch the graph of

$$y = \tan 2x°$$

for $0 \leqslant x \leqslant 180$.

7 Given that

$$y = 5 \sin x°$$

for $0 \leqslant x \leqslant 360$, find

(a) the maximum value of y and the value of x for which y is a maximum.

(b) the minimum value of y and the value of x for which y is a minimum.

8 Solve the equation

$$5 \cos x° = 3$$

in the range $-180° \leqslant x \leqslant 180°$.

Test yourself

What to review

If your answer is incorrect:

1 Find two different values of x between 0° and 360° for which

$$3\cos x = 1$$

Review Higher book Unit 13, page 250, Example 11.

---

2 Draw the graph of $y = \sin 2x°$ for $0 \leqslant x \leqslant 180°$.

Review Higher book Unit 13, page 248, Worked examination question.

---

3 Find the maximum value of $5 \sin 2x°$.

Review Higher book Unit 13, page 248, Worked examination question.

Answers to Test yourself

1 $x = 70.5°, 289.5°$

2

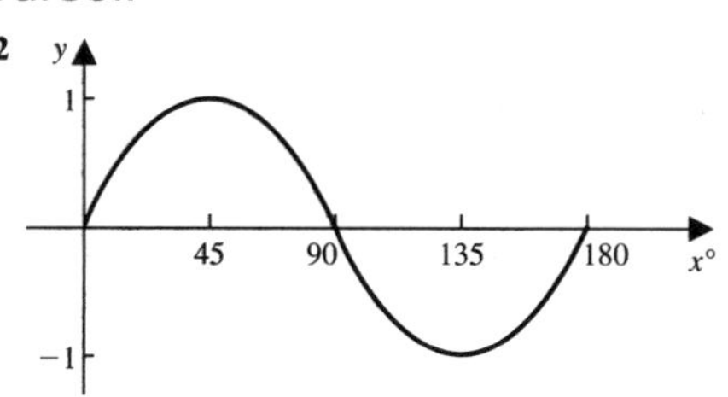

3 5

16 Combined transformations

It is possible to combine two (or more) transformations – such as reflections, rotations, enlargements – to create an equivalent single transformation.

Key points to remember

1 An object can be transformed by:

- a translation
- a reflection
- a rotation
- an enlargement

2 Two transformations can be combined to form a single equivalent transformation.

3 A reflection followed by a reflection can be replaced by the single transformation of:

- a rotation if the reflection lines are *not* parallel.
- a translation if the reflection lines are parallel.

Example 1

Triangle A is rotated through $90°$ in the anticlockwise direction about $(1, 0)$ to give the image B.

B is then rotated through $90°$ in the anticlockwise direction about the origin to form the second image C.

Work out the single transformation which transforms A to C.

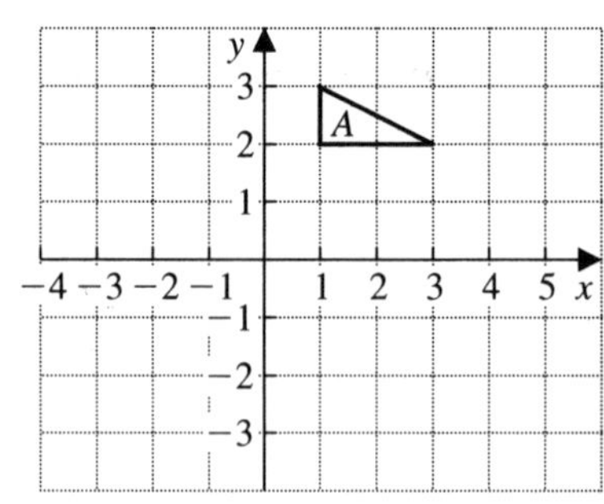

Answer

Rotating A about $(1, 0)$ through $90°$ anticlockwise gives B as in the diagram.

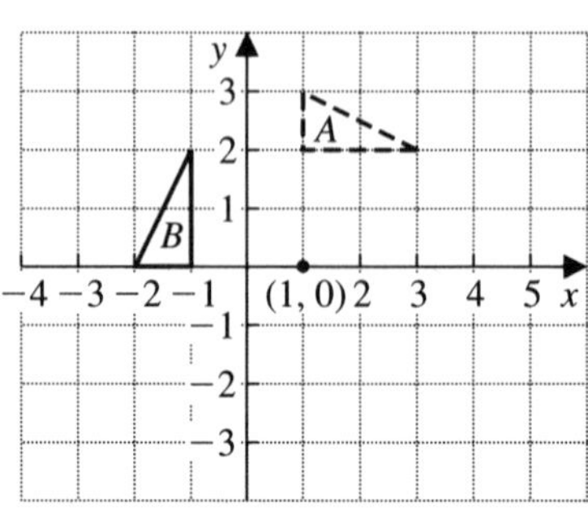

Then rotating B about $(0, 0)$ in the anticlockwise direction gives C.

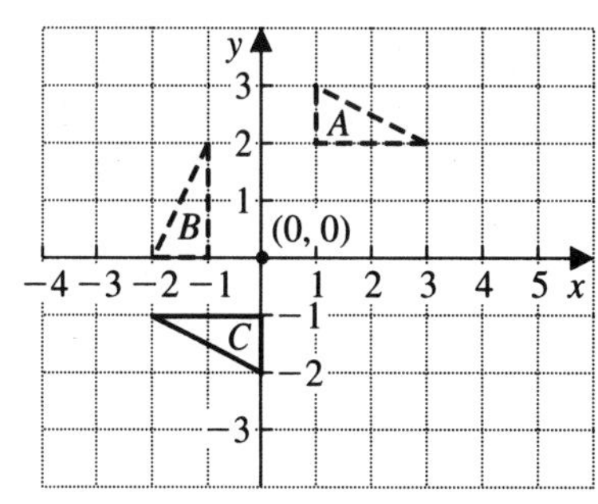

Using **2** the single transformation which transforms A to C is a rotation through 180°.
The centre of the rotation is found at the intersection of the construction lines.

So the single transformation that transforms A to C is a rotation through 180° about $(\frac{1}{2}, \frac{1}{2})$.

Note: the single transformation could also be described as an enlargement, scale factor −1, centre $(\frac{1}{2}, \frac{1}{2})$.

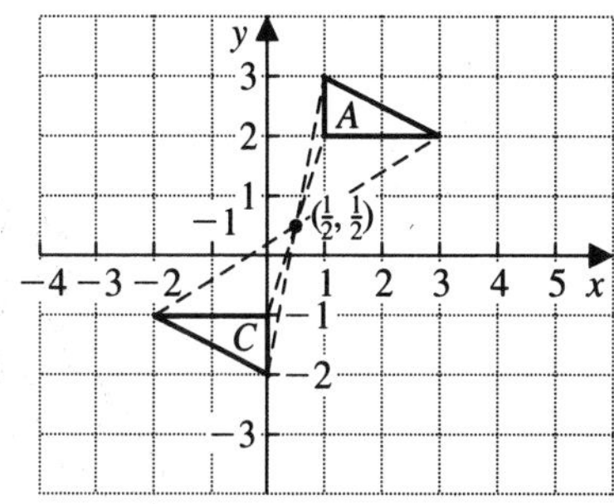

Worked examination question [L]

The triangle T is reflected in the y-axis to form the image S.

S is then reflected in the line $y = -x$ to form the second image U.

Find the single transformation which maps T to U.

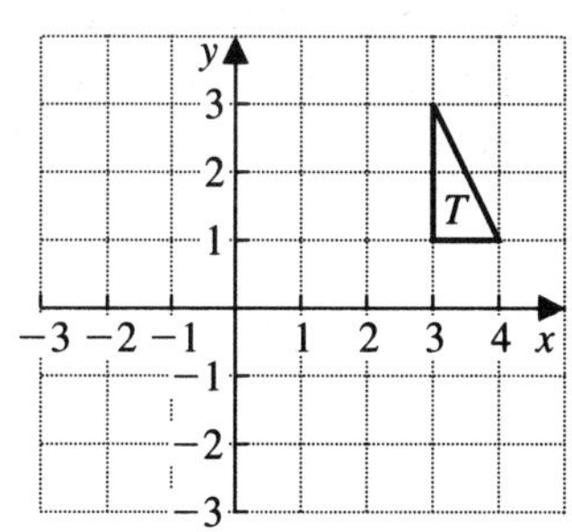

Answer

Reflecting T in the y-axis gives S, and then reflecting S in the line $y = -x$ gives U.

Using **3** the single transformation which maps T to U is a rotation about the origin through 90° in the anticlockwise direction.

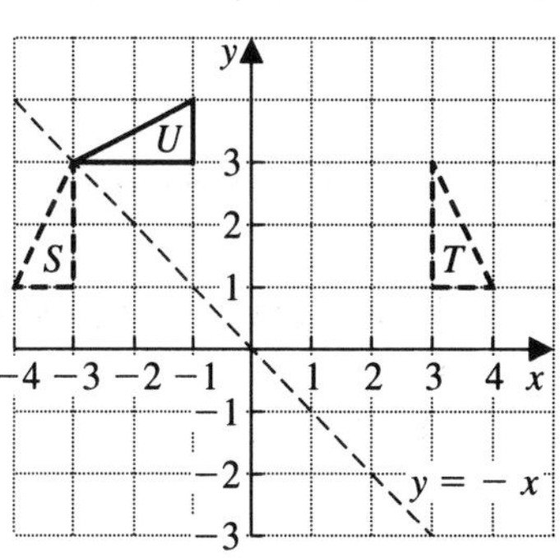

Example 2

The triangle A is reflected in the line L to form an image A'. A' is then reflected in the line M to form a second image A''. Work out the single transformation which maps A to A''.

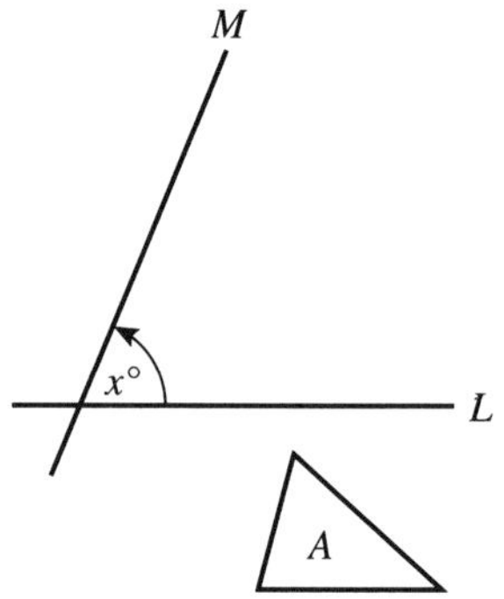

Answer

Reflecting A in L gives A'.

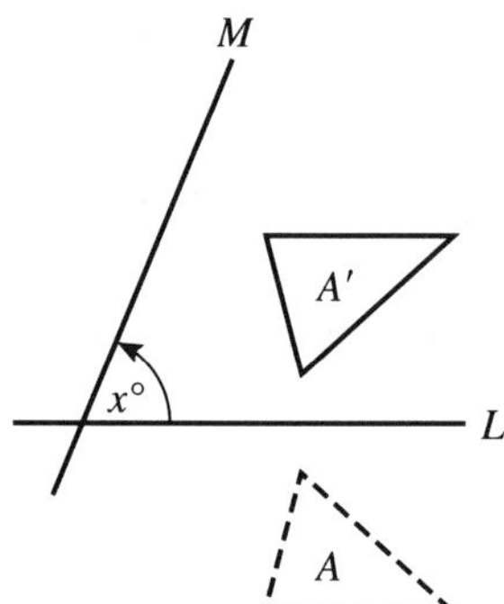

Reflecting A' in M gives A''.

The single transformation which maps A to A'' is a rotation about the point of intersection of L and M, through $2x°$ in the anticlockwise direction.

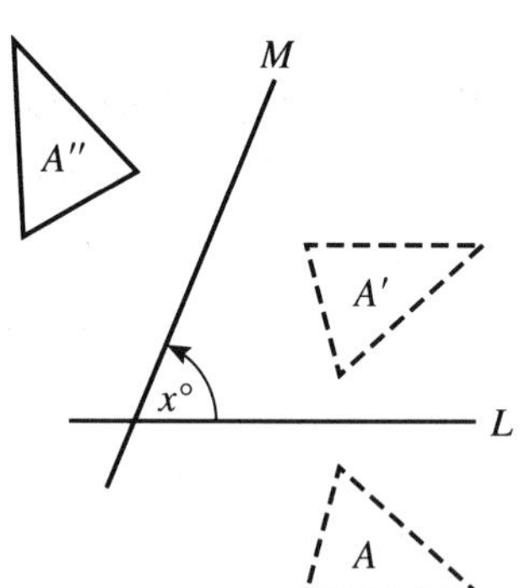

Revision exercise 16

1 Triangle T is reflected in the line $x = 3$ to produce the image S.

S is then reflected in the line $x = 6$ to produce a second image U.

Find the single transformation which maps
(a) T to U
(b) U to T.

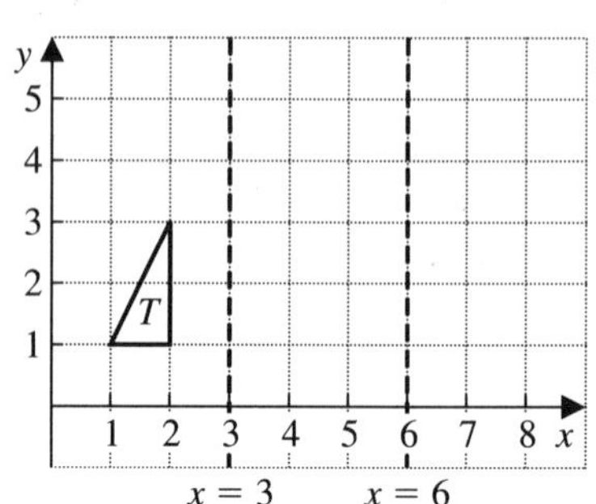

2 **(a)** Draw diagrams to show how the outcome of two successive reflections can be
either
(i) a translation or **(ii)** a rotation.
(b) In case **(ii)** above, describe completely the rotation.

3 The triangle A is rotated about $(-1, 0)$ through $90°$ in the clockwise direction to produce the image A'.

A' is then rotated about $(0, 0)$ through $90°$ in the clockwise direction to produce the second image A''.

Find the single transformation which transforms
(i) A to A''
(ii) A'' to A.

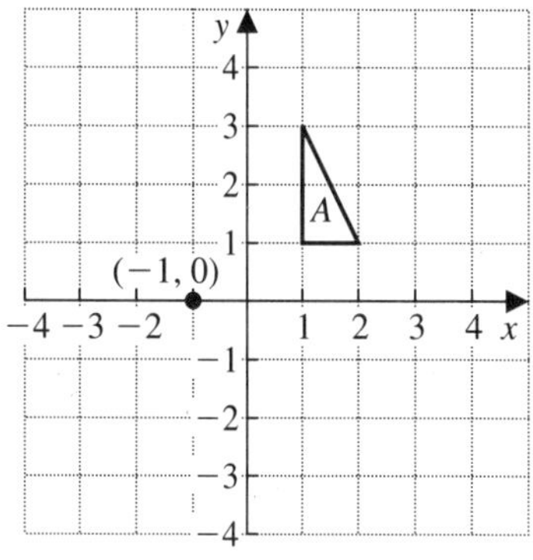

4 A shape S is reflected in the x-axis to produce an image S'. S' is then reflected in the line $y = x$ to produce a second image S''.

Describe fully the single transformation which maps S to S''.

5 A triangle ABC has co-ordinates

$$A(1, 1) \quad B(2, 1) \quad C(1, 3).$$

ABC is enlarged by scale factor 2, centre (0, 0) to produce an image $A'B'C'$.
$A'B'C'$ is then enlarged by scale factor 3, centre (0, 0) to produce $A''B''C''$.

(a) Find the coordinates of the vertices of $A''B''C''$.
(b) Find the single transformation which maps ABC to $A''B''C''$.

6 A shape S is enlarged by a scale factor k, centre point X, to produce an image S'.
S' is then enlarged by a scale factor k, centre point X, to produce a second image S''.

Find the single transformation which maps
(a) S to S''
(b) S'' to S.

Test yourself

What to review

1 The diagram shows two lines L and M and a shape S.
The two lines L and M intersect at the point P.
The acute angle between L and M is 72°.

S is reflected in L to produce an image S'.
S' is then reflected in M to produce a second image S''.

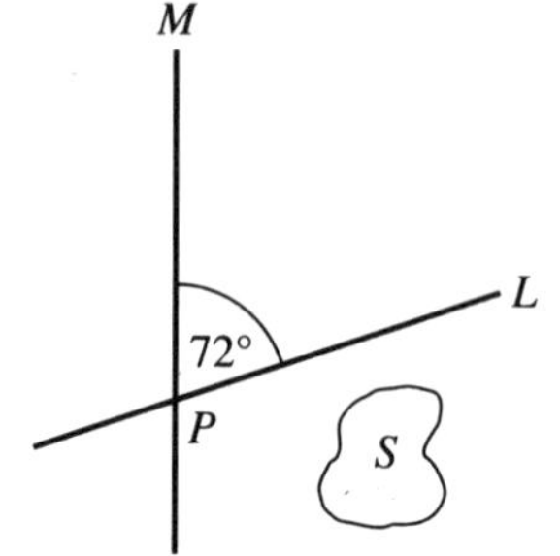

Describe fully the single transformation which maps S to S''.

If your answer is incorrect:

Review Higher book Unit 6, page 130, Section 6.4.

---

2 Triangle T is rotated about (0, 0), through 90° in the clockwise direction to produce an image T'.
T' is then rotated about (0, 0), through 45° in the clockwise direction to produce a second image T''.

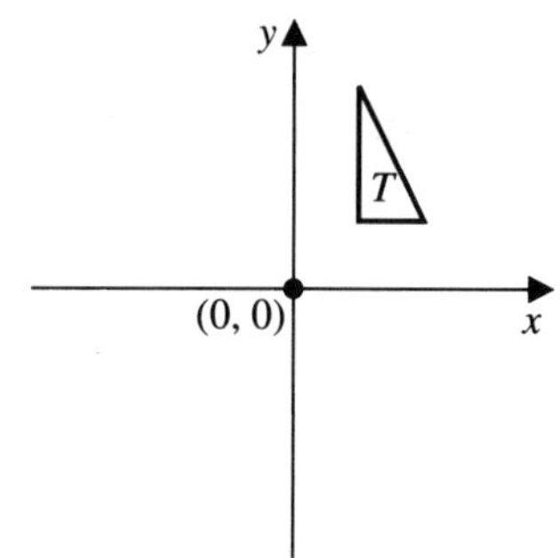

Describe fully the single transformation which maps T'' to T.

Review Higher book Unit 6, page 125, Example 5 and page 130, Section 6.4.

Answers to Test yourself

1 Anticlockwise rotation about P through 144°.
2 Rotation about (0, 0), through 135° in the anticlockwise direction.

17 Advanced mensuration

Key points to remember

1 The formulae for parts of a circle are:

- arc length $= \dfrac{\pi r\theta}{180}$
- area of sector $= \dfrac{\pi r^2\theta}{360}$
- area of segment $= \dfrac{\pi r^2\theta}{360} - \dfrac{1}{2}r^2 \sin\theta$

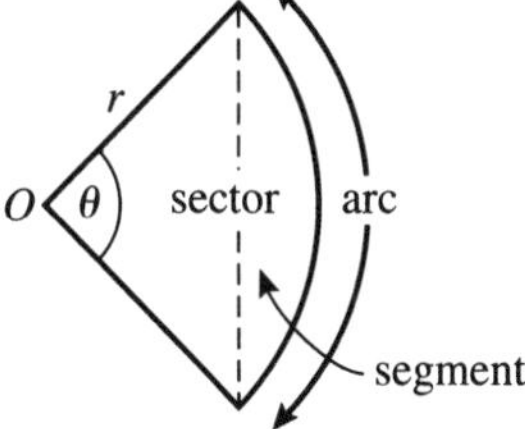

2 The formulae for a cylinder are:

- surface area $= 2\pi rh + 2\pi r^2$
- volume $= \pi r^2 h$

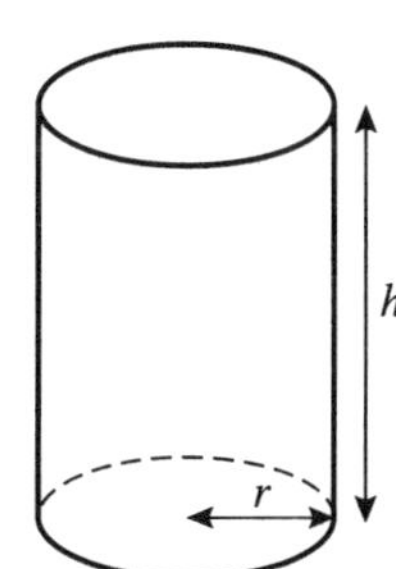

3 The volume of a pyramid or cone

$$= \frac{1}{3} \times \text{area of base} \times \text{vertical height}$$

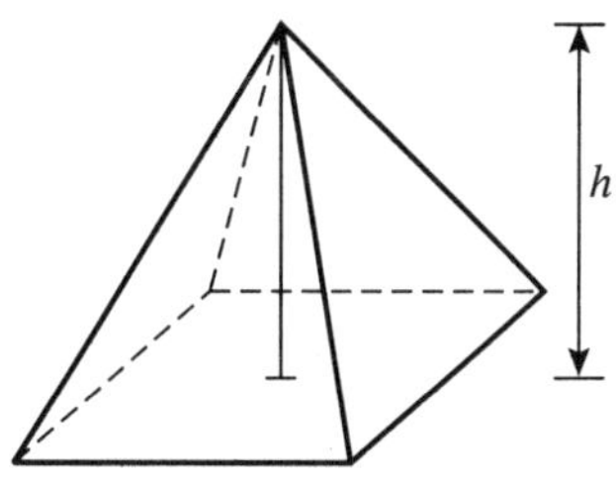

4 The formulae for a sphere are:

- volume $= \dfrac{4\pi r^3}{3}$
- surface area $= 4\pi r^2$

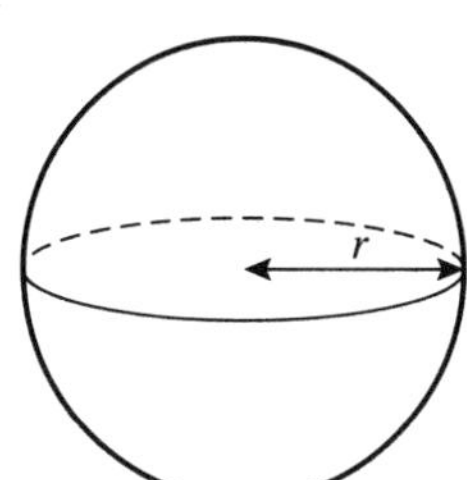

5 When a shape is enlarged by a scale factor k to produce a similar shape:

- area of enlarged shape $= k^2 \times$ area of original shape
- volume of enlarged shape $= k^3 \times$ volume of original shape.

Example 1

The diagram is a sketch of a 'standard' size box of chocolates.

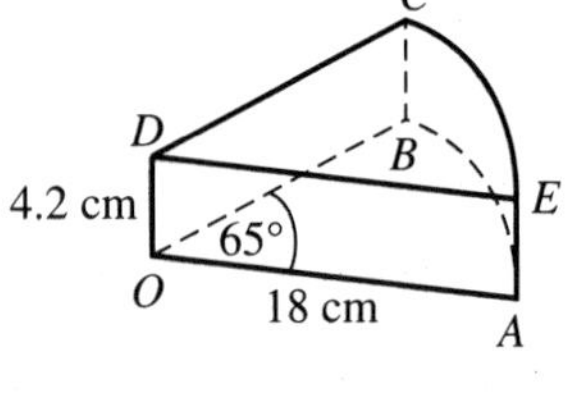

The height of the box is 4.2 cm.
The base OAB is a sector of a circle, centre O.
The radius of the circle is 18 cm and the angle $AOB = 65°$.

Calculate
(a) the arc length AB.
(b) the volume of the box.
(c) the surface area of the box.

An 'economy' size box of chocolates is similar in shape to the 'standard' size box.
The lengths of the 'economy' size box are all 15% greater than the corresponding lengths of the sides of the 'standard' size box.

(d) Calculate the volume of the 'economy' size box.

Answer

(a) Using **1**

$$\text{arc } AB = \frac{\pi \times 18 \times 65}{180} = 20.42 \text{ cm (2 d.p.)}$$

(b) Volume of box = area of base × height

volume of prism = area of base × height

Using **1**

$$\text{Area of sector (base)} = \frac{\pi \times 18^2 \times 65}{360} = 183.78 \text{ cm}^2 \text{ (2 d.p.)}$$

So Volume $= 183.78 \times 4.2 = 771.89 \text{ cm}^3$

(c) Total surface area of box = area of base + area of top + area of $OAED$ + area of $OBCD$ + area of curved face $AECB$

Area of base = area of top = 183.78 cm^2 (from (a))

Area of $OAED$ = area of $OBCD$ = $18 \times 4.2 = 75.6 \text{ cm}^2$

Area of curved surface = arc length AB × height
$= 20.42 \times 4.2 = 85.76 \text{ cm}^2$

So total surface area =
$183.78 + 183.78 + 75.6 + 75.6 + 85.76 = 604.52 \text{ cm}^2$

(d) Length of 'economy' box = 1.15 × length of 'standard'
So the 'standard' box is enlarged by a scale factor of 1.15 to give the 'economy' size box.

Using **5**
Volume of 'economy' box $= 1.15^3 \times$ volume of 'standard' box
$= 1.15^3 \times 771.89$
$= 1173.95 \text{ cm}^3$

Worked examination question [L]

A solid metal right circular cone has a height of 12.7 cm and a diameter of 9.4 cm.

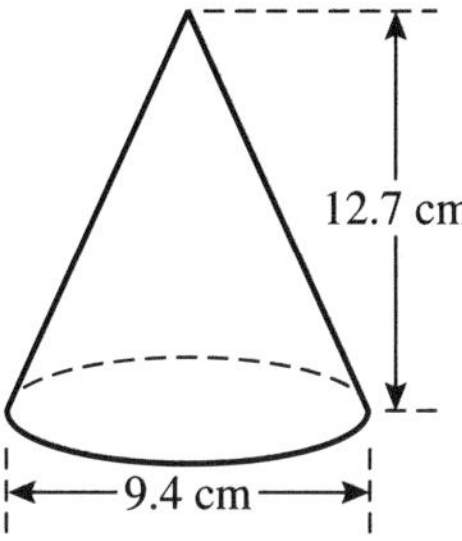

(a) Calculate the volume of the cone.

The cone is melted down and re-cast as a sphere.
During this process none of the metal is lost.
(b) Calculate the radius of the sphere.
(c) Calculate the surface area of the sphere.

Answer

(a) Using **3**

volume $= \frac{1}{3} \times$ area of base $\times$ height

area of base $= \pi \times 4.7^2$

area of circle $= \pi r^2$

So volume $= \frac{1}{3} \times \pi \times 4.7^2 \times 12.7 = 293.78\,\text{cm}^3$

(b) Using **4**

volume of sphere $= \frac{4}{3}\pi r^3$

So $\frac{4}{3}\pi r^3 = 293.78$

So $r^3 = \dfrac{3 \times 293.78}{4\pi}$

$= 70.135$

and $r = \sqrt[3]{70.135}$

$= 4.12\,\text{cm}$

(c) Using **4**

surface area of sphere $= 4\pi r^2$

$= 4 \times \pi \times 4.12^2$

$= 213.31\,\text{cm}^2$

Revision exercise 17

1 Two similar boxes have volumes of $2000\,\text{cm}^3$ and $16\,000\,\text{cm}^3$.
The area of the base of the larger box is $60\,\text{cm}^2$.
Calculate the area of the base, in cm^2, of the smaller box. [L]

2 A rock band festival is to be held in a park.
The diagram represents the part of the park which will be fenced off to enclose the audience.

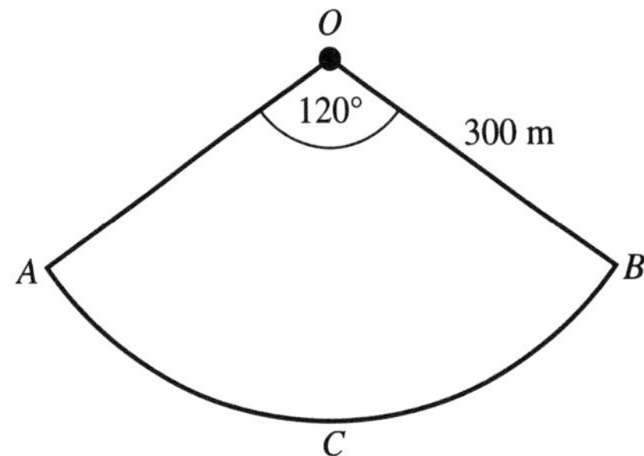

Diagram NOT accurately drawn

$OACB$ is a sector of a circle, centre O, radius 300 m.
Angle AOB equals 120°.

(a) Calculate the total length of the perimeter of the fence. Give your answer correct to the nearest 10 metres.

The police are worried about the safety of the audience. They have said that each person should have at least $3\,\text{m}^2$ of grass area.

(b) Calculate the maximum audience allowed to attend the festival. Give your answer to the nearest 100.

3 A cone has a circular base of diameter 16 cm.
The slant height of the cone is 17 cm.
Calculate the volume of the cone.

4 $VABC$ is a tetrahedron. V is vertically above B.
Angle $ABC = 90°$ $AB = 9\,\text{cm}$ $BC = 12\,\text{cm}$
The volume of $VABC = 360\,\text{cm}^3$
Calculate
(a) VB **(b)** VA

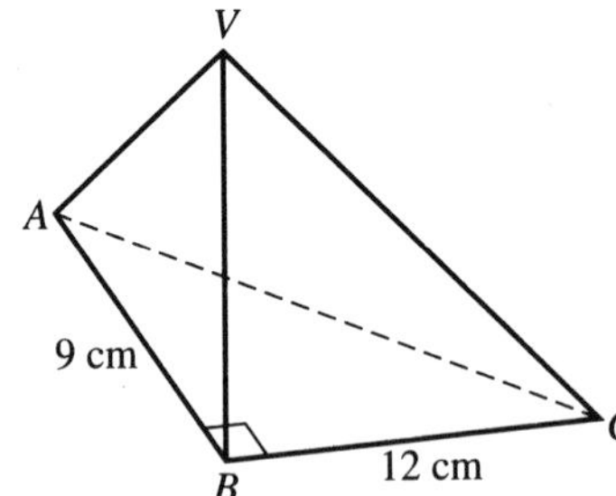

5 The surface area of a sphere is $340\,\text{cm}^3$.

Calculate:
(a) the radius of the sphere
(b) the volume of the sphere.

6 $VABCD$ is a square-based pyramid.
$AB = 12\,\text{cm}$ $VA = 20\,\text{cm}$

Calculate the volume of $VABCD$.

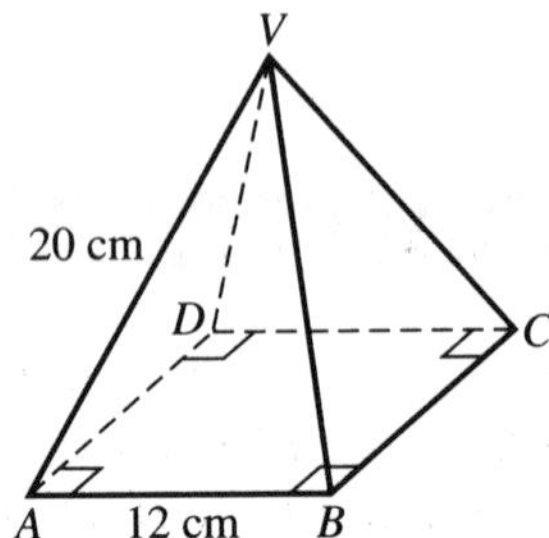

7 *Koke* is sold in two sizes of bottles.
These are called '**standard size**' and '**extra size**'.
The 'standard size' and 'extra size' bottles are similar in shape.

The capacity of a 'standard size' bottle is 1 litre.

The capacity of an 'extra size' bottle is 1.5 litres.

The height of an 'extra size' bottle is 32 cm.

Calculate the height of a 'standard size' bottle.

(A capacity of 1 litre is equivalent to a volume of 1000 cm^3.)

8 The diagram is a sketch of a solid paperweight.
The paperweight consists of a right circular cone on a hemispherical base.
The diameter of the base of the cone and the diameter of the hemispherical base are both equal to 8 cm.
The overall height of the paperweight is 14 cm.

Calculate:

(a) the volume of the paperweight

(b) the mass of the paperweight, given that it is made from oak of density 0.9 g cm^{-3}.

8 cm

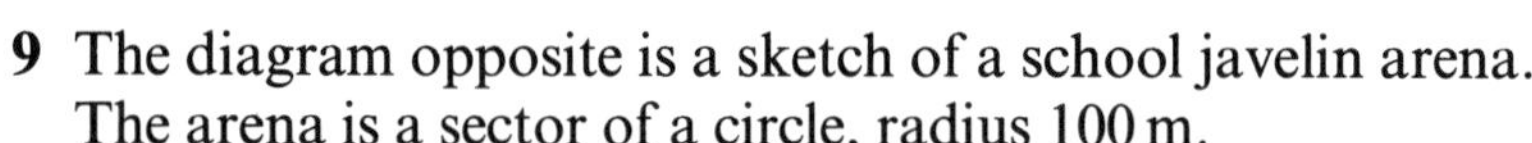

9 The diagram opposite is a sketch of a school javelin arena.
The arena is a sector of a circle, radius 100 m.

Calculate

(a) the perimeter of the arena

(b) the area of the arena.

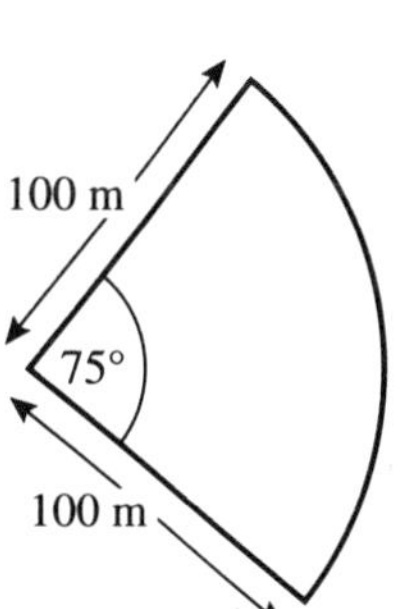

10 A cone has a height of 18 cm and the radius of its base is 3 cm.

(a) Calculate the volume of the cone.

The measurements of the cone are correct to the nearest millimetre.

(b) Write down the lower bound of the radius of the cone.

(c) Calculate the difference between the upper and lower bounds of the volume of the cone expressed as a percentage of the volume of the cone found in part (a). [L]

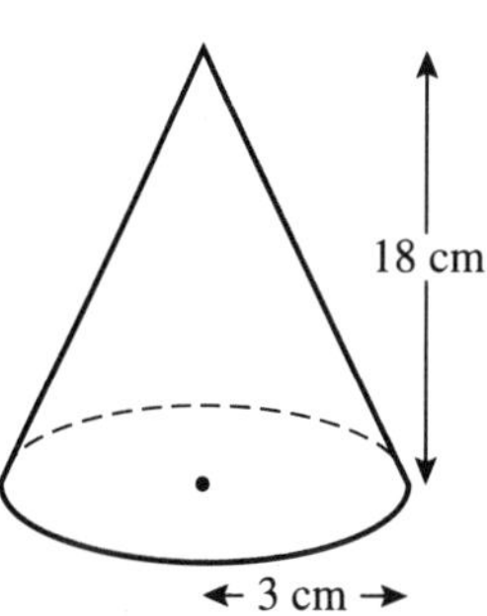

There is more about upper and lower bounds in Unit 4.

Test yourself | What to review

1 Two containers P and Q are similar.

If your answer is incorrect:

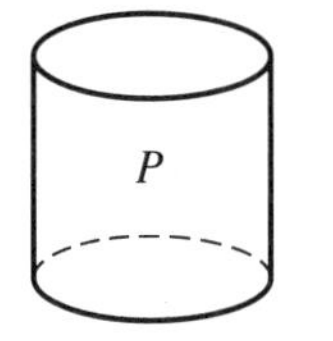

The surface area of container P is $2000\,\text{cm}^2$.
The surface area of container Q is $125\,\text{cm}^2$.
The volume of container P is $4000\,\text{cm}^3$.

Calculate the volume of container Q. [L, adapted]

Review Higher book Unit 19, page 349, Section 19.3.

---

2 There is a light security system.
The system can detect movement inside a sector of a circle.
The radius of the circle is 24 m.
The sector angle is 125°.

Calculate the area of the sector. [L, adapted]

Review Higher book Unit 19, page 337, Example 3.

---

3 A solid silver rod is in the shape of a cylinder of height 15 cm.
The diameter of its base is 8 cm.

(a) Calculate the volume of the cylinder.

Review Higher book Unit 19, page 343, Example 6.

The silver is melted down and re-cast as a solid cone of height 32 cm. During this process none of the silver is lost.

(b) Calculate the radius of the circular base of the cone.

Review Higher book Unit 19, pages 345–7.

Answers to Test yourself

1 $62.5\,\text{cm}^3$ **2** $628.32\,\text{m}^2$ **3** **(a)** $753.98\,\text{cm}^3$ **(b)** 4.74 cm

18 Vectors

Any quantity, such as velocity or force, which has both magnitude (size) and direction is called a vector.

A quantity which has a numerical value only – and can be represented by a number – is called a scalar.

Key points to remember

1 A vector can be represented as

$$\begin{pmatrix} x \\ y \end{pmatrix}$$

or $\overrightarrow{AB}$

or **a**

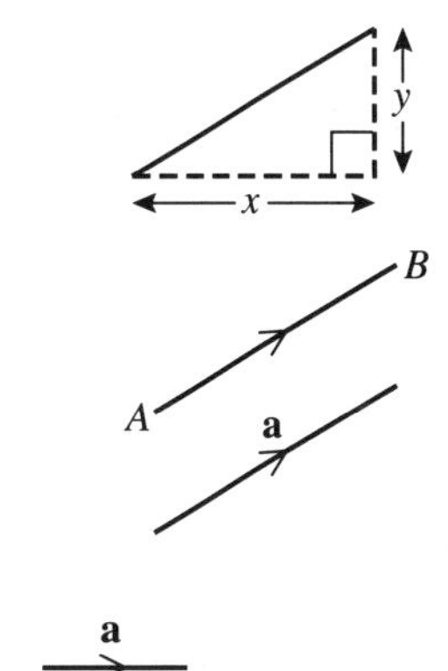

2 The vector $k\mathbf{a}$, where k is a scalar, is parallel to **a** and has length

$$k \times \text{length of } \mathbf{a}$$

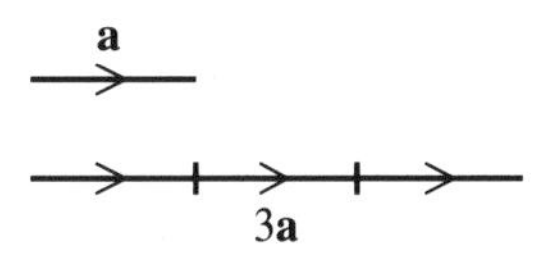

3 $\mathbf{a} + \mathbf{b}$ is found by the parallelogram law for addition.

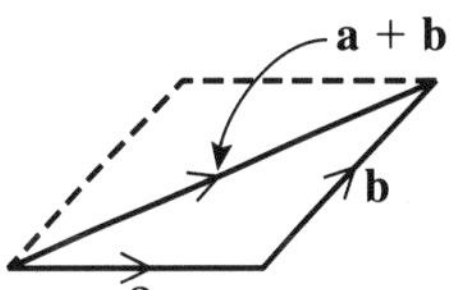

4 $\mathbf{a} - \mathbf{b}$ is found by:

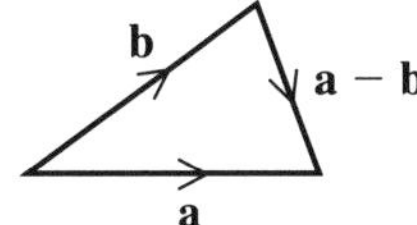

5 The **position** vector of a point P is $\overrightarrow{OP}$, where O is usually the origin.

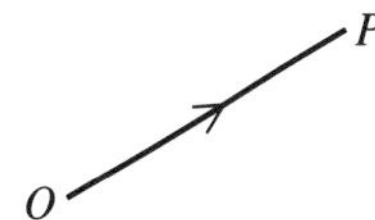

6 If A and B have position vectors **a** and **b** respectively then **the vector** $\overrightarrow{AB} = \mathbf{b} - \mathbf{a}$

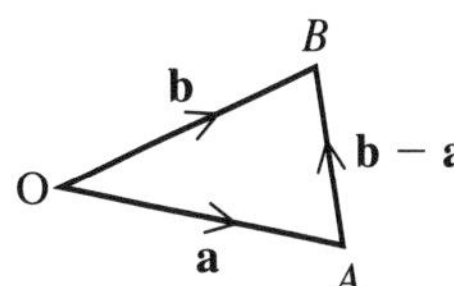

7 If A and B have position vectors **a** and **b** respectively then the position vector of the midpoint, M, of the line joining A to B is

$$\overrightarrow{OM} = \mathbf{m} = \tfrac{1}{2}(\mathbf{a} + \mathbf{b})$$

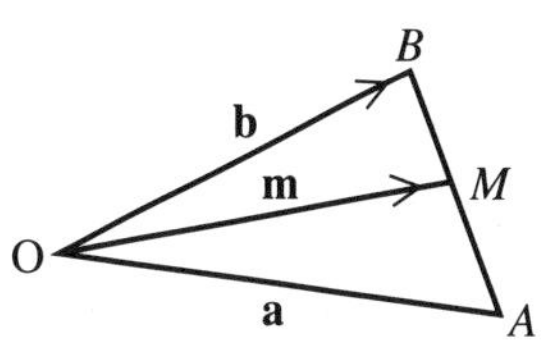

Example 1

ABC is an equilateral triangle.
M is the midpoint of AC.

$$\overrightarrow{AB} = \mathbf{a} \qquad \overrightarrow{BC} = \mathbf{b}$$

Work out, in terms of **a** and **b**, expressions for the vectors:

(i) $\overrightarrow{AC}$ (ii) $\overrightarrow{MB}$

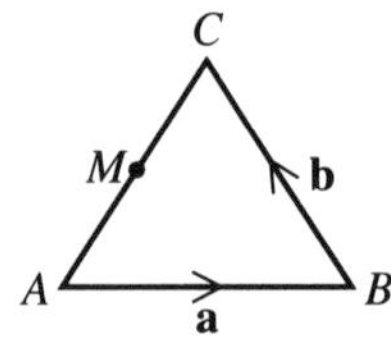

Answer

(i) Using **3**

$$\overrightarrow{AC} = \overrightarrow{AB} + \overrightarrow{BC}$$

So $\overrightarrow{AC} = \mathbf{a} + \mathbf{b}$

(ii) Using **2**

$$AM = \tfrac{1}{2}AC$$

So $\overrightarrow{AM} = \tfrac{1}{2}\overrightarrow{AC}$

$$\overrightarrow{AM} = \tfrac{1}{2}(\mathbf{a} + \mathbf{b})$$

Using **3**

$$\overrightarrow{AM} + \overrightarrow{MB} = \overrightarrow{AB}$$

So $\overrightarrow{MB} = \overrightarrow{AB} - \overrightarrow{AM}$

$$\overrightarrow{MB} = \mathbf{a} - \tfrac{1}{2}(\mathbf{a} + \mathbf{b}) = \tfrac{1}{2}\mathbf{a} - \tfrac{1}{2}\mathbf{b}$$

$$= \tfrac{1}{2}(\mathbf{a} - \mathbf{b})$$

Worked examination question 1 [L]

$$\overrightarrow{PQ} = \begin{pmatrix} 2 \\ 3 \end{pmatrix} \quad \overrightarrow{QR} = \begin{pmatrix} 4 \\ 5 \end{pmatrix} \quad \overrightarrow{TS} = \begin{pmatrix} 3 \\ 4 \end{pmatrix}$$

(a) Show that PR is parallel to TS.
(b) Write down the ratio of the length of PR to the length of TS.

Answer

(a) Using **3**

$$\overrightarrow{PR} = \overrightarrow{PQ} + \overrightarrow{QR}$$

$$= \begin{pmatrix} 2 \\ 3 \end{pmatrix} + \begin{pmatrix} 4 \\ 5 \end{pmatrix} = \begin{pmatrix} 6 \\ 8 \end{pmatrix} = 2\begin{pmatrix} 3 \\ 4 \end{pmatrix}$$

$$\overrightarrow{PR} = 2\overrightarrow{TS}$$

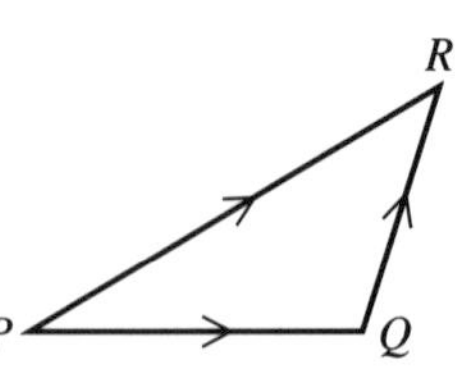

So from **2**

PR is parallel to TS

(b) Using **2**

length of $PR = 2 \times$ length of TS

or length PR : length $TS = 2:1$

Worked examination question 2 [L]

ABCDE is a regular pentagon.

$$\overrightarrow{AB} = \mathbf{p}, \quad \overrightarrow{BC} = \mathbf{q}, \quad \overrightarrow{CD} = \mathbf{r}$$

(a) In terms of **p**, **q** and **r**, find expressions for
(i) $\overrightarrow{AC}$ (ii) $\overrightarrow{AD}$

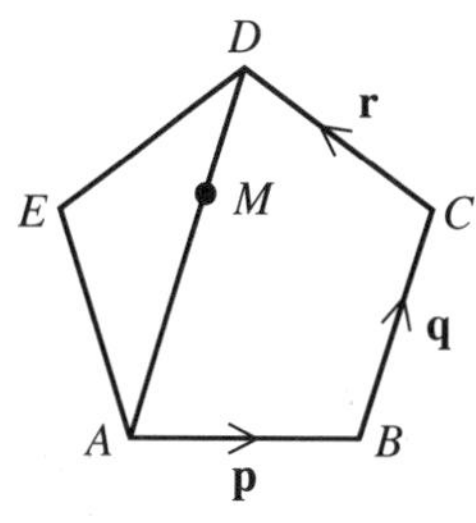

M is the point on AD such that $DM = \frac{1}{3}DA$.

(b) Find expressions for
(i) $\overrightarrow{AM}$ **(ii)** $\overrightarrow{MC}$

Answer

(a) (i) Using **3**

$$\overrightarrow{AC} = \overrightarrow{AB} + \overrightarrow{BC}$$

So $$\overrightarrow{AC} = \mathbf{p} + \mathbf{q}$$

(ii) Using **3** again

$$\overrightarrow{AD} = \overrightarrow{AB} + \overrightarrow{BC} + \overrightarrow{CD}$$
$$\overrightarrow{AD} = \mathbf{p} + \mathbf{q} + \mathbf{r}$$

(b) (i) $$DM = \tfrac{1}{3}DA$$

So $$AM = \tfrac{2}{3}AD$$

Using **2**

$$\overrightarrow{AM} = \tfrac{2}{3}\overrightarrow{AD}$$
$$= \tfrac{2}{3}(\mathbf{p} + \mathbf{q} + \mathbf{r})$$

(ii) Using **3**

$$\overrightarrow{AM} + \overrightarrow{MC} = \overrightarrow{AC}$$
$$\overrightarrow{MC} = \overrightarrow{AC} - \overrightarrow{AM}$$

so

$$MC = (\mathbf{p} + \mathbf{q}) - \tfrac{2}{3}(\mathbf{p} + \mathbf{q} + \mathbf{r})$$
$$= \mathbf{p} + \mathbf{q} - \tfrac{2}{3}\mathbf{p} - \tfrac{2}{3}\mathbf{q} - \tfrac{2}{3}\mathbf{r}$$
$$= \tfrac{1}{3}\mathbf{p} + \tfrac{1}{3}\mathbf{q} - \tfrac{2}{3}\mathbf{r}$$

Revision exercise 18

1 The vectors $\overrightarrow{OP}$ and $\overrightarrow{OQ}$ are given by

$$\overrightarrow{OP} = \begin{pmatrix} 3 \\ 2 \end{pmatrix} \quad \text{and} \quad \overrightarrow{OQ} = \begin{pmatrix} 2 \\ -1 \end{pmatrix}$$

(a) Draw the vectors $\overrightarrow{OP}$ and $\overrightarrow{OQ}$ on a grid.

(b) Find the vector

$$\overrightarrow{OP} + \overrightarrow{OQ}$$

and draw it on your grid.

(c) Find the vector $\overrightarrow{OP} - \overrightarrow{OQ}$ [L]

2 $\mathbf{a} = \begin{pmatrix} -2 \\ 4 \end{pmatrix}$ $\mathbf{b} = \begin{pmatrix} 3 \\ 2 \end{pmatrix}$ $\mathbf{c} = \begin{pmatrix} 5 \\ 6 \end{pmatrix}$

Show that $\mathbf{a} + 4\mathbf{b}$ is parallel to $\mathbf{c}$.

3 A is the point with coordinates (2, 5).
B is the point with coordinates (6, 7).
M is the midpoint of AB
O is the origin.
Work out the position vector $\overrightarrow{OM}$.

4 ABC is a triangle

$$AB = \mathbf{a}, \quad BC = \mathbf{b}$$

(a) Find an expression, in terms of $\mathbf{a}$ and $\mathbf{b}$ for AC.

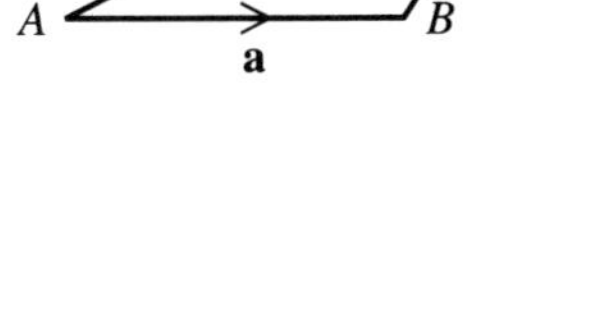

P is the point on AB such that $AP = \frac{2}{3}AB$.
Q is the point on AC such that

$$AQ : QC = 2:3$$

(b) Find an expression in terms of $\mathbf{a}$ and $\mathbf{b}$ for $\overrightarrow{PQ}$.
(c) Explain whether or not PQ is parallel to BC.

5 In the diagram

$$AB = 3AS, \; BT = \tfrac{1}{2}BC, \; SC = 4SX$$
$$\overrightarrow{AS} = \mathbf{a}, \; \overrightarrow{BT} = \mathbf{b}$$

Find, in terms of $\mathbf{a}$ and $\mathbf{b}$, expressions for

(a) $\overrightarrow{SB}$ **(b)** $\overrightarrow{AT}$ **(c)** $\overrightarrow{SC}$ **(d)** $\overrightarrow{AX}$

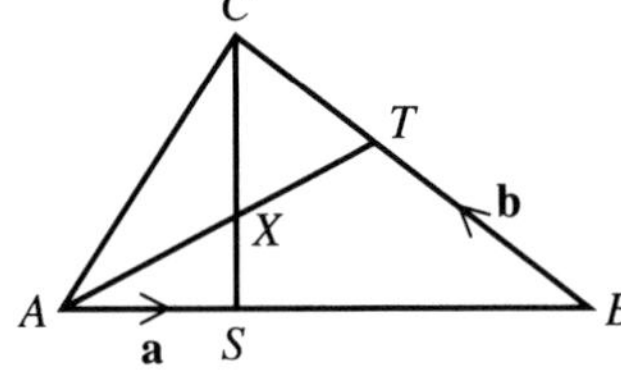

6 The diagram shows a triangle ABC.
P is the midpoint of AB and Q is the point on AC such that $QC = 2AQ$.

$$\overrightarrow{AP} = \mathbf{x} \text{ and } \overrightarrow{AQ} = \mathbf{y}$$

(a) Write $\overrightarrow{PQ}$ in terms of $\mathbf{x}$ and $\mathbf{y}$.
T is a point such that $\overrightarrow{AT} = \overrightarrow{BC}$.
(b) Show that PQT is a straight line [L]

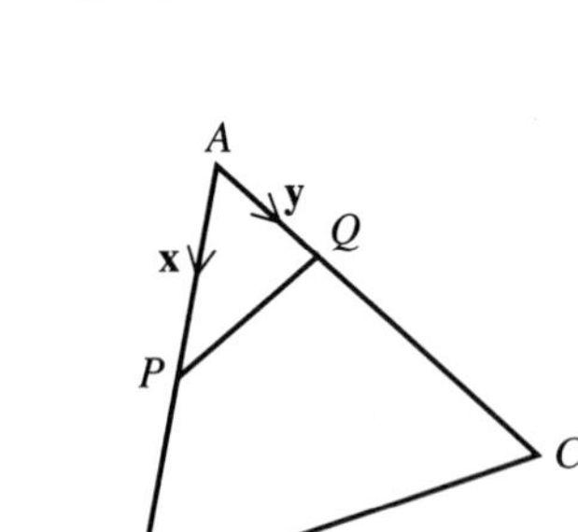

7 In the diagram, Q is the midpoint of the side PR and T is the midpoint of the side PS of the triangle PRS.

$$\overrightarrow{PQ} = \mathbf{a}, \quad \overrightarrow{PT} = \mathbf{b}$$

(a) Write down, in terms of $\mathbf{a}$ and $\mathbf{b}$, the vectors
(i) $\overrightarrow{QT}$ (ii) $\overrightarrow{PR}$ (iii) $\overrightarrow{RS}$

(b) Write down one geometrical fact about QT and RS which could be deduced from your answers to part **(a)** [L]

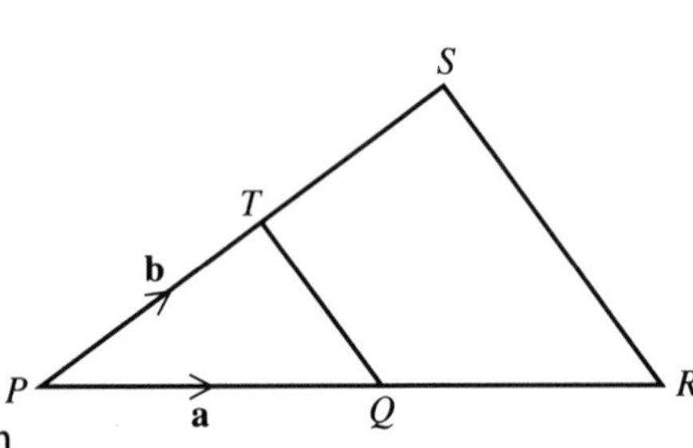

Test yourself | What to review

1 $\overrightarrow{OP} = \begin{pmatrix} -3 \\ 4 \end{pmatrix}$; $\overrightarrow{OR} = \begin{pmatrix} 5 \\ 6 \end{pmatrix}$

If your answer is incorrect:

and M is the midpoint of PR.

(a) Find $\overrightarrow{PR}$

Review Higher book Unit 26, page 477, Examples 7 and 8.

(b) Find $\overrightarrow{OM}$

Review Higher book Unit 26, page 477, Examples 8 and 9.

(c) Find the vector $\overrightarrow{OQ}$ such that $OPQR$ is a parallelogram.

Review Higher book Unit 26, page 476, Section 26.6.

---

2 $ABCD$ is a trapezium.
DC is a parallel to AB.

$$DC = 3AB$$

$ABPQ$ is a parallelogram

$$\overrightarrow{AB} = \mathbf{a},\ \overrightarrow{AD} = \mathbf{b},\ \overrightarrow{AQ} = \mathbf{c}$$

In terms of **a**, **b** and **c**, find expressions for

(a) vector $\overrightarrow{DC}$

Review Higher book Unit 26, page 473, Section 26.5.

(b) vector $\overrightarrow{AC}$

Review Higher book Unit 26, page 473, Section 26.5.

(c) vector $\overrightarrow{BC}$

Review Higher book Unit 26, page 473, Section 26.5.

(d) vector $\overrightarrow{PC}$

Review Higher book Unit 26, page 473, Section 26.5.

Answers to Test yourself

1 (a) $\begin{pmatrix} 8 \\ 2 \end{pmatrix}$ **(b)** $\begin{pmatrix} 1 \\ 5 \end{pmatrix}$ **(c)** $\begin{pmatrix} 2 \\ 10 \end{pmatrix}$

2 (a) 3**a** **(b)** **b** + 3**a** **(c)** **b** + 2**a** **(d)** **b** + 2**a** − **c**

19 Circle theorems

You should know and be able to use each of these theorems.

Key points to remember

1 The perpendicular bisector of any chord passes through the centre of the circle.

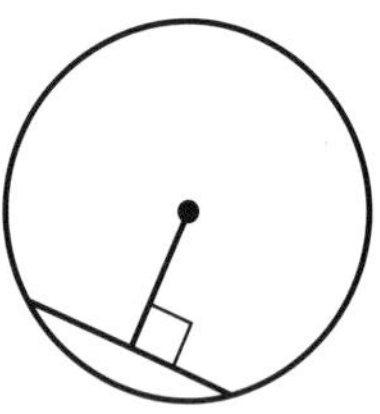

2 The angle between a tangent and a radius is 90°.

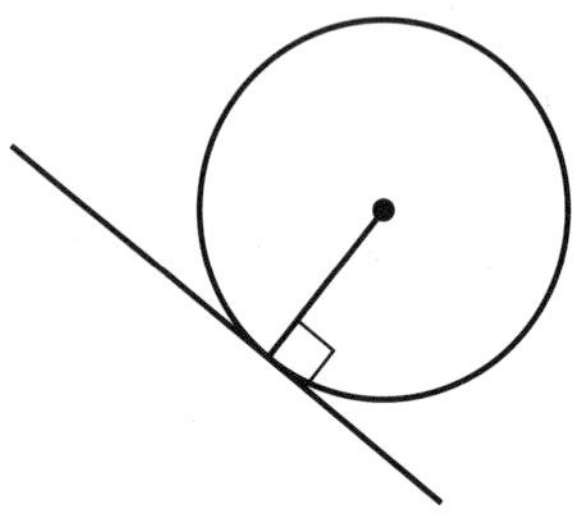

3 The lengths of the two tangents from a point are equal.
For example, $PT = PS$

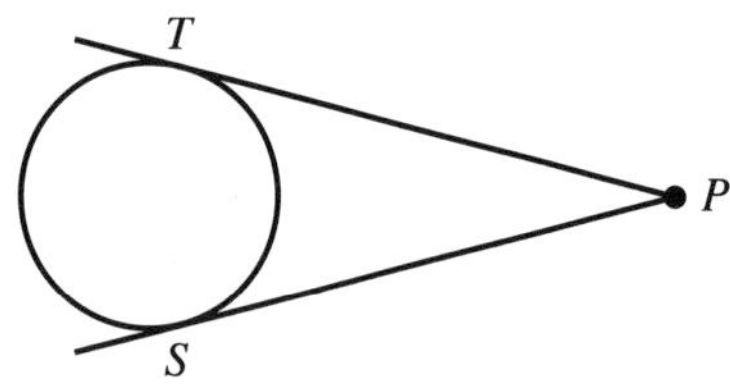

4 The angle in a semicircle is always a right angle.

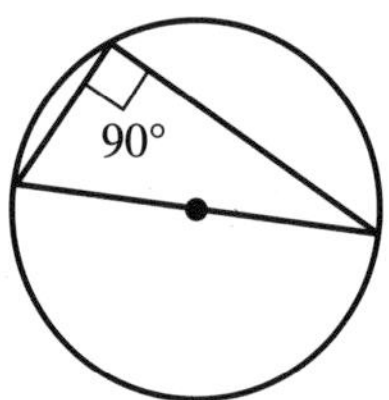

5 The angle at the centre is twice the angle at the circumference, for example:

$$A\hat{O}B = 2 \times A\hat{C}B$$

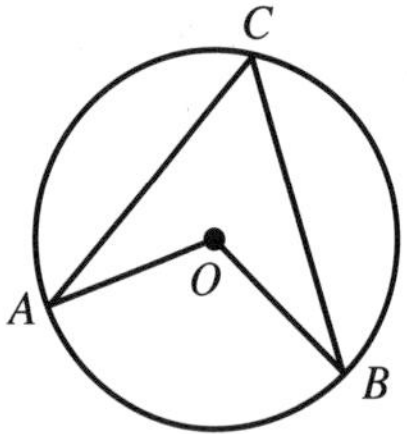

6 Angles in the same segment are equal, for example:

$$A\hat{C}B = A\hat{D}B$$

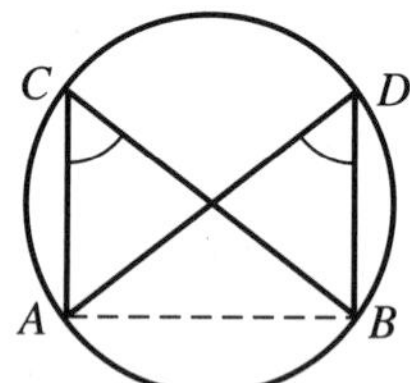

7 Opposite angles of a cyclic quadrilateral are supplementary.
For example,

$$x + y = 180°$$

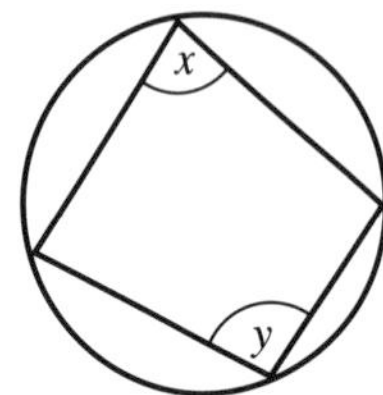

8 The angle between a tangent and its chord is equal to the angle in the alternate segment. For example,

$$a = b$$

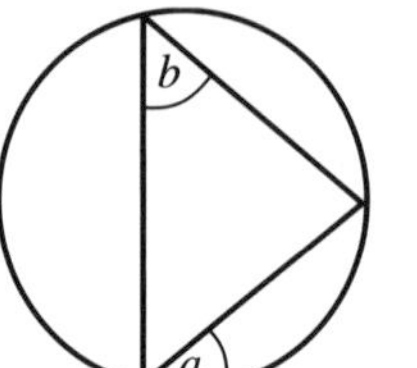

This is called the alternate segment theorem.

Example 1

PT is a tangent to the circle, centre *O*.
Angle $T\hat{O}B = 110°$

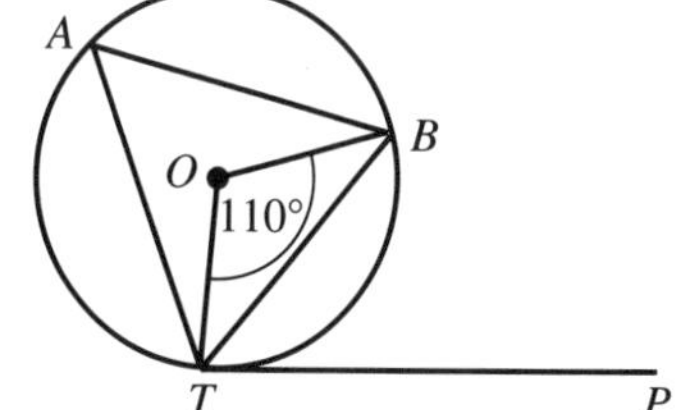

Calculate the angle *BTP*.
Give reasons for your calculation.

Answer

Using **8**

angle $BTP =$ angle BAT (alternate segment)

Also, using **5**

angle $BAT = \frac{1}{2}$ of angle TOB (angle at centre)

So angle $BAT = \frac{1}{2}$ of $110°$

$= 55°$

so angle $BTP = 55°$

Worked examination question [L]

The line *ABC* is a tangent to the circle at *B*.
Angle $FBD = 85°$ and angle $BEF = 31°$

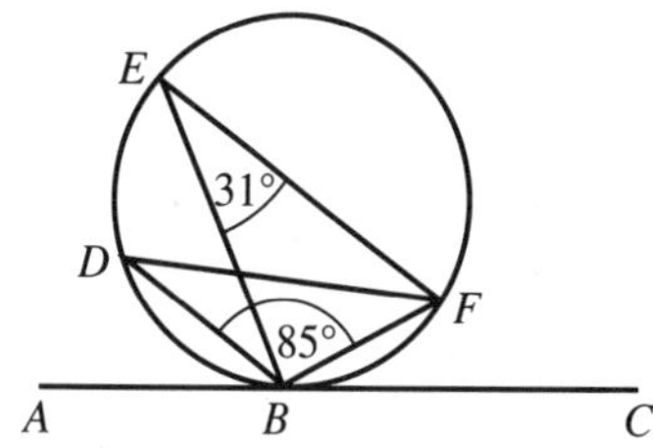

Calculate the size of angle *ABD*.
Give reasons for your calculation.
Show all steps in your working.
You may get some credit for finding any angle in the diagram provided you give a reason.

Answer

Using **8**

angle $FBC =$ angle BEF (alternate segment)

So angle $FBC = 31°$

Also angle $ABD +$ angle $FBD +$ angle $FBC = 180°$ (straight line)

So angle $ABD + 85° + 31° = 180°$

angle $ABD + 116° = 180°$

angle $ABD = 64°$

Revision exercise 19

1 In the diagram, *SU* is a diameter of the circle centre *O*.
PT is a tangent to the circle at *T*.
QST and *QVU* are straight lines.
Angle $STP = 56°$
Angle $SQV = 17°$

Find the size of angle *VUS*.

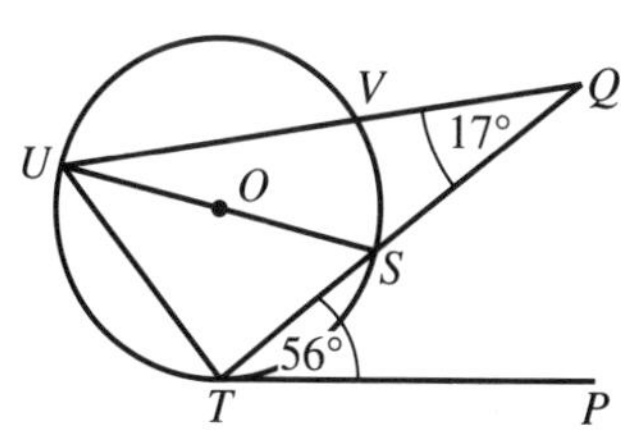

2 AB is a tangent to a circle, centre O.
Angle $BOD = 124°$
Angle $CDB = 31°$

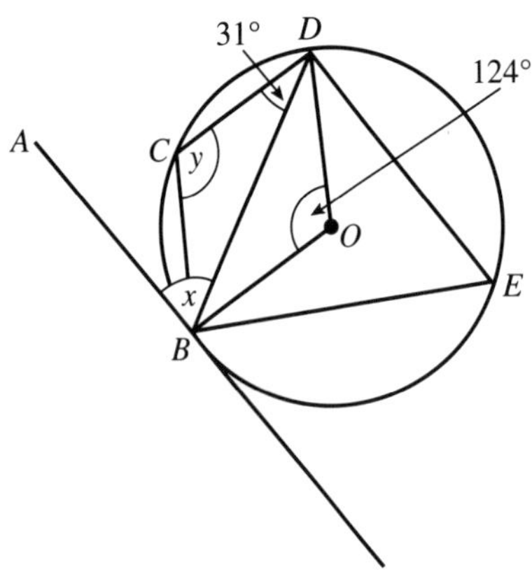

Calculate the sizes of the angles marked x and y.

3 Points A, B, C and D lie on the circumference of a circle.
TC is a tangent.
AD is parallel to BC.
Angle $BAD = 85°$
Angle $TCD = 47°$

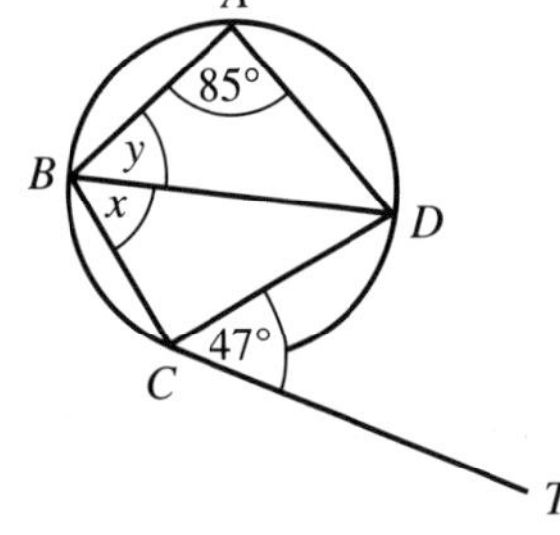

Calculate the angles marked
(a) x **(b)** y

4 $ABCD$ is a cyclic quadrilateral.
The line PAQ is a tangent at A to the circle.
AB extended meets DC extended at the point X.
$BD = BX$
Angle $DAQ = 48°$
Angle $XCB = 70°$

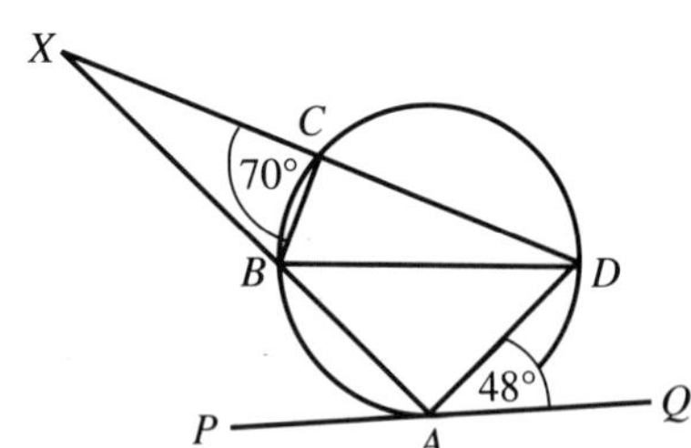

Giving your reasons, find the sizes of the angles:
(a) $A\hat{B}D$ **(b)** $B\hat{A}D$ **(c)** $X\hat{B}D$ **(d)** $C\hat{D}B$

5 BC, AB and AC are tangents to the circle at D, E and F respectively.
The angle $EBD = x°$
The angle $FCD = y°$

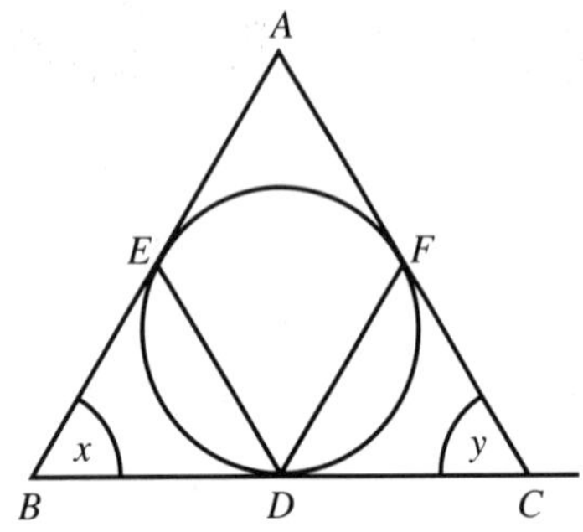

Giving your reasons, find an expression in x and y for the angle EDF.

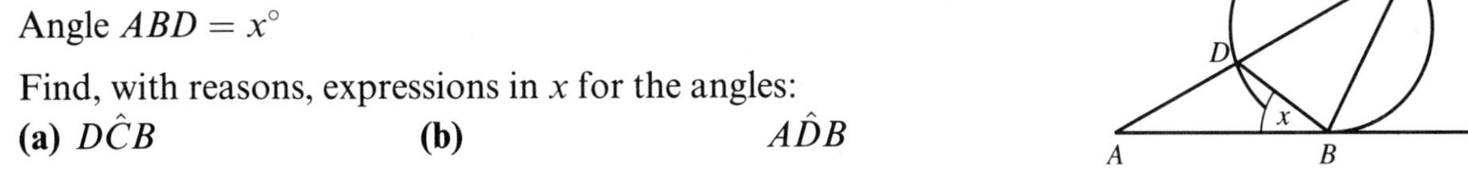

6 AB is a tangent to the circle at the point B.
$BC = BD$
Angle $ABD = x°$

Find, with reasons, expressions in x for the angles:
(a) $D\hat{C}B$ **(b)** $A\hat{D}B$

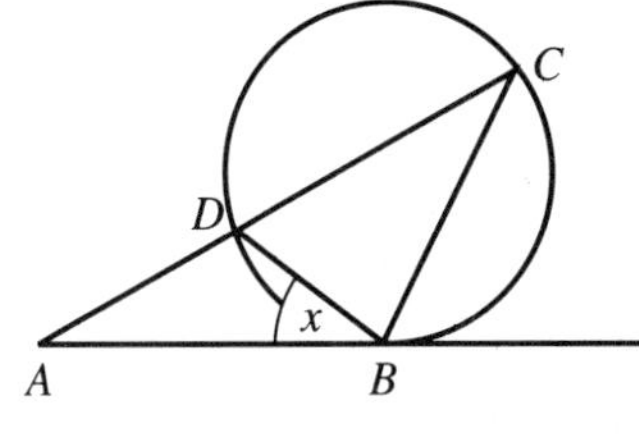

7 TP and TQ are tangents from T to the circle, centre O.
(a) Explain why it is possible to draw a circle which passes through all four of the points O, P, T and Q.

Angle $PTQ = 50°$, $OP = 12$ cm.
(b) Calculate the length of the radius of the circle through $OPTQ$.
Give your answer to the nearest millimetre.

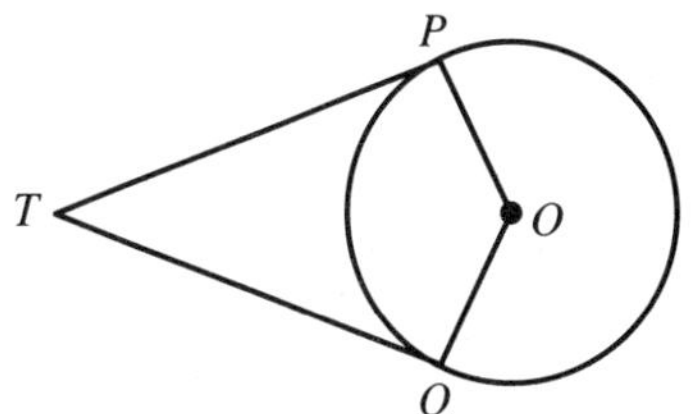

Test yourself

What to review

1 $ABCD$ and E lie on the circumference of a circle centre O.
COE is a diameter of the circle.
PA is a tangent to the circle at A.
$CD = ED$
Angle $EAP = 36°$

If your answer is incorrect:

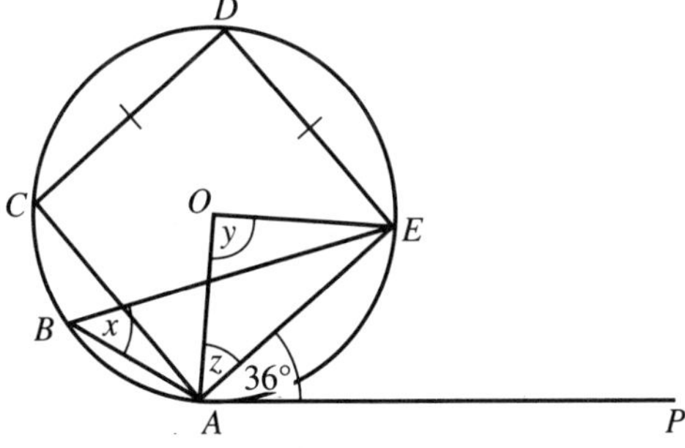

Find:
(a) angle x — *Review Higher book Unit 28, page 516, Section 28.6.*

(b) angle y — *Review Higher book Unit 28, page 509, Section 28.3.*

(c) angle z — *Review Higher book Unit 28, page 503, Example 3.*

Answers to test yourself

1 **(a)** $x = 36°$ **(b)** $y = 72°$ **(c)** $z = 54°$

20 Sampling

Sampling techniques are used to collect statistics when it is unrealistic to obtain the views of an entire population or test all of the components being manufactured.

Key points to remember

1 A random sample is one in which each member of the population is equally likely to be selected.

2 A stratified sample is one in which the population is divided into groups called strata and each stratum is randomly sampled.

3 A selective sample is one in which every nth item is chosen, where n is selected at random.

Example 1

There are 1200 pupils at Marriott School.
660 of the pupils are girls.
540 of the pupils are boys.

The Headteacher of the school, Mrs Lukin, wishes to find out if the pupils would like her to set up a 'School Council' which has pupil representation.

Mrs Lukin decides to take a sample of the views of the pupils. She needs to have information about the views of the girls and the boys.

Mrs Lukin has time to interview 50 pupils to obtain their views.

Explain how Mrs Lukin could design a sampling method to obtain the views of the girls and boys at her school.

Answer

The population of the school is divided into two groups – girls and boys. Using **2**, Mrs Lukin needs to use a stratified sampling technique.

Of the pupils at the school, 660 are girls, so the proportion of girls is:

$$\frac{660}{1200} = 0.55$$

So in the 50 pupils she interviews there should be:

$0.55 \times 50 = 27.5$ girls

and $50 - 27.5 = 22.5$ boys

She cannot interview 0.5 of a pupil, so she should toss a coin to decide whether to interview
either 28 girls and 22 boys
or 27 girls and 23 boys.

Once she has decided on (say) 28 girls, she could take a random sample of 28 out of the 660 girls. One way of doing so could be to put all 660 girls' names in a hat and select 28 of them – without looking.

Then she could repeat this process with the boys' names, but selecting only 22 names.

Worked examination question [L]

There are 200 members of the Martineau Golf Club.
Their age ranges and gender are given in the table below.

Age (a) years	Frequency	
	Male	Female
$0 \leqslant a < 20$	20	10
$20 \leqslant a < 40$	48	34
$40 \leqslant a < 60$	42	28
$60 \leqslant a < 80$	12	6

The club captain decides to conduct a survey of the members, in order to obtain their views about the building of a new club house. He wishes his sample size to be about 50 of the club members and to take account of their ages and gender.

(a) How many males should there be in the sample?
Give your answer correct to the nearest whole number.

(b) How many of the sample should be aged under 40 years?
Give your answer correct to the nearest whole number.

(c) How many of the sample should be females aged between 20 years and 40 years?
Give your answer correct to the nearest whole number.

Answer

As a fraction, or decimal, of the total number of members, the 50 to be sampled is

$$\frac{50}{200} = \frac{1}{4} \text{ or } 0.25$$

(a) Using **2** the stratum of males has a total of

$$20 + 48 + 42 + 12 = 122$$

So there need to be

$$0.25 \times 122 = 30.5$$

30 or 31 males should be included in the sample.

(b) Using **2** the stratum of members aged under 40 has a total of

$$20 + 10 + 48 + 34 = 112$$

So there need to be

$$0.25 \times 112 = 28$$

28 members in the sample should be under 40.

(c) Using **2** the stratum of females aged between 20 and 40 has a total of 34.

So there need to be

$$0.25 \times 34 = 8.5$$

8 or 9 females aged between 20 and 40 should be included in the sample.

Example 2

Explain how to take a selective sample of 4% of electrical components from a production line.

Answer

$$4\% = \frac{4}{100} = \frac{1}{25}$$

To take a 4% sample you select 1 in every 25 items and test them.
Choose a number at random between 1 and 25 – say it is n.
Then, using **3** sample the nth, $(n + 25)$th, $(n + 50)$th, ..., etc component from the production line.

Revision exercise 20

1 There are 1600 pupils at Manor High School.
The table shows how these pupils are distributed by year group and gender.

Year group	Number of boys	Number of girls
7	158	164
8	149	162
9	171	158
10	160	162
11	162	154

Joan is conducting a survey about pupils' favourite hobbies.
She decides to use a stratified random sample of 200 pupils according to year group and gender.

(a) How many year 11 girls should there be in her sample?
(b) How many year 8 boys should there be in her sample?

2 Explain how to take a selective sample of 5% of the 1200 pupils at Lucea High School.

3 There are 40 000 people who can vote in an election. They are categorised according to age and gender as in the table below.

Age range (years)	Number of males	Number of females
Under 35	7800	8300
35 or over	12 600	11 300

Just before the election, a market research company makes a survey of the voting intentions of these people. They will try to obtain the views of 2400 people.

Work out the number in the sample who should be
(a) female aged under 35 **(b)** male **(c)** aged 35 or over.

Test yourself

What to review

1 There are 12 000 students at Lucea College.

If your answer is incorrect:

The table shows how the students are distributed by type of course and gender.

Course type	Number of males	Number of females
Full-time	2400	2600
Part-time	3800	3200

The college management team decide to obtain the views of the students on a proposed new car-parking scheme.

Describe how the management team could take a sample of 240 students so that it will be representative of the views of male, female, full-time and part-time students.

Review Higher book Unit 4, page 70.

2 Explain how you could take a selective sample of 10% of the names from an electoral register.

Review Higher book Unit 4, page 71.

Answers to Test yourself

1 Stratified sample with numbers as below:

Course type	Male	Female
full-time	48	52
part-time	76	64

2 Take a random number from 1 to 10 – call it n. Then sample nth, $(n + 10)$th, $(n + 20)$th, etc. names.

21 Mean for frequency tables

Sometimes discrete or continuous data is grouped into class intervals. You can estimate the mean from grouped data.

Key points to remember

1 An estimate of the mean for grouped data is:

$$\bar{x} = \frac{\Sigma fx}{\Sigma f}$$

where x is the midpoint of each class interval and f is the frequency.

2 To draw a frequency polygon, you plot the frequency against the midpoint of each class interval and join the points with straight lines.

Worked examination question [L]

The grouped frequency table gives information about the weekly rainfall (d) in millimetres at Heathrow Airport in 1995.

Weekly rainfall (d) in mm	Number of weeks
$0 \leqslant d < 10$	20
$10 \leqslant d < 20$	18
$20 \leqslant d < 30$	6
$30 \leqslant d < 40$	4
$40 \leqslant d < 50$	2
$50 \leqslant d < 60$	2

(a) Calculate an estimate for the mean weekly rainfall.
(b) Draw the frequency polygon for this information.

Answer

(a) Using **1** we find the midpoints of each class interval (the x column) and multiply these by the frequency for each interval.

Weekly rainfall (d) in mm	Number of weeks (f)	Midpoint x	fx
$0 \leqslant d < 10$	20	5	100
$10 \leqslant d < 20$	18	15	270
$20 \leqslant d < 30$	6	25	150
$30 \leqslant d < 40$	4	35	140
$40 \leqslant d < 50$	2	45	90
$50 \leqslant d < 60$	2	55	110
	Total $\Sigma f = 52$		Total $\Sigma fx = 860$

$$\text{Estimate of mean} = \frac{\Sigma fx}{\Sigma f}$$

$$= \frac{860}{52}$$

$$= 16.54\,\text{mm}$$

(b) Using **2** the frequency polygon is:

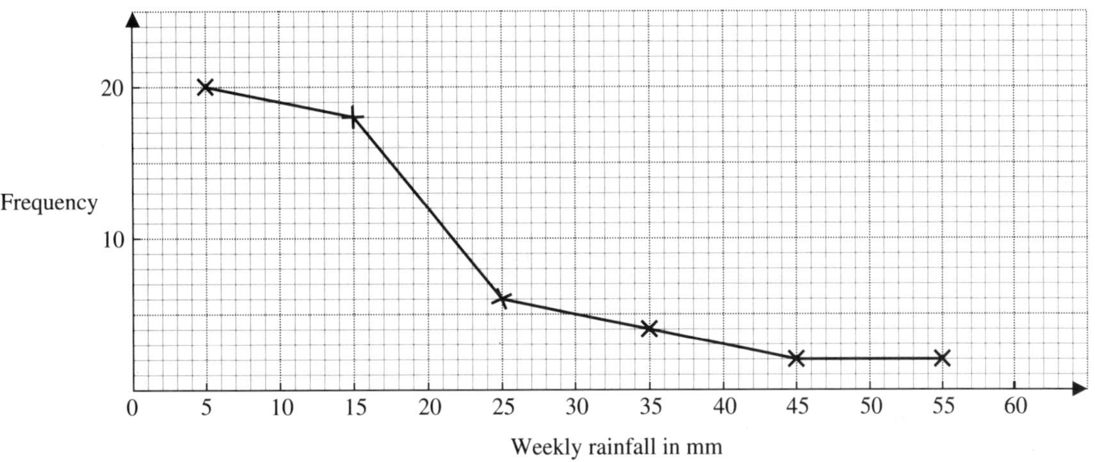

Revision exercise 21

1 Bronwen owns a pet shop.
The table gives information about the weights of hamsters in Bronwen's shop.

Weight w of hamster in grams	Number of hamsters
$28 \leqslant w < 30$	9
$30 \leqslant w < 32$	5
$32 \leqslant w < 34$	4
$34 \leqslant w < 36$	2

Calculate an estimate for the mean weight of the hamsters in Bronwen's shop.

2 A survey was carried out in Mathstown High School to find out how long it takes the pupils to travel to school.

The results of the survey are shown in the table.

Time, t minutes, to travel to school	Number of pupils
$0 < t \leqslant 10$	14
$10 < t \leqslant 20$	12
$20 < t \leqslant 30$	19
$30 < t \leqslant 40$	5
Total	50

(a) Write down the modal interval for the pupils.

(b) Work out an estimate for the mean time taken for the pupils to travel to school.

(c) Draw a frequency polygon for this information. [L]

Remember the mode is the most frequent value.

3 A bag contains 20 potatoes. The weights of these potatoes are shown in the frequency table.

Weight (w) grams	Frequency
$100 < w \leqslant 200$	4
$200 < w \leqslant 300$	6
$300 < w \leqslant 400$	9
$400 < w \leqslant 500$	1

Work out an estimate for the mean weight of the potatoes in the bag.

4 Asurvey was carried out to find out how much time was needed by a group of pupils to complete homework set on a particular monday evening.

The results are shown in the table below.

Time, t hours, spent on homework	Number of pupils
0	3
$0 < t \leqslant 1$	14
$1 < t \leqslant 2$	17
$2 < t \leqslant 3$	5
$3 < t \leqslant 4$	1

Calculate an estimate for the mean time spent on homework by the pupils in the group. [L]

Test yourself

What to review

1 The table shows the frequency distribution of marks scored by 100 candidates in a Science examination.

If your answer is incorrect:

Marks	Frequency
0–9	3
10–19	5
20–29	12
30–39	20
40–49	24
50–59	18
60–69	12
70–79	6

(a) Calculate an estimate of the mean mark.

Review Higher book Unit 15, page 275, Example 3.

(b) Draw a frequency polygon to illustrate the data.

Review Higher book Unit 4, page 72, Section 4.7.

Answers to Test yourself

1 (a) 43.4 **(b)**

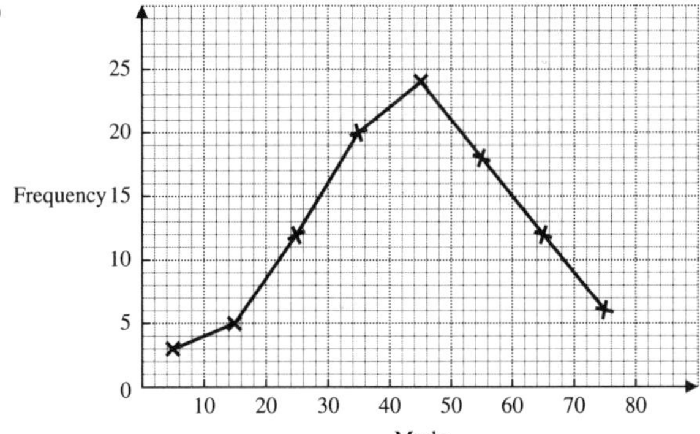

22 Cumulative frequency curves

The cumulative frequency curve is used to estimate the median, some measures of spread and various proportions for data in a grouped frequency table or distribution.

Key points to remember

1 The median is the middle value of the distribution.

2 The lower quartile is the value one quarter of the way into the distribution.

3 The upper quartile is the value three quarters of the way into the distribution.

4 Interquartile range
= upper quartile − lower quartile

5 The cumulative frequency curve can be used to find the percentage or proportion of the whole distribution lying between two values.

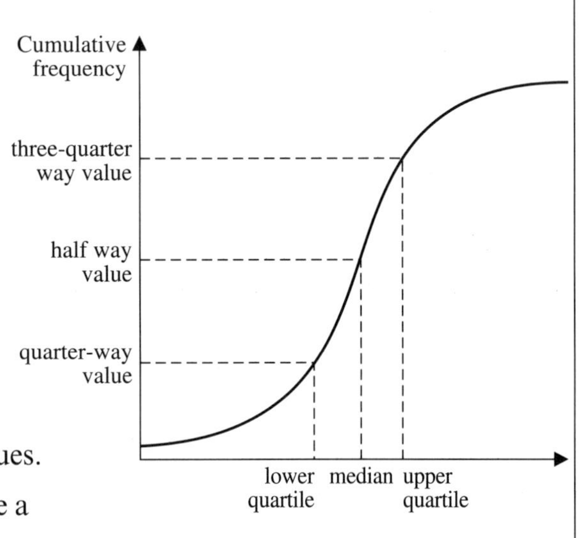

6 To compare two distributions you should use a measure of average and a measure of spread.

Example 1

Lucea Golf Club has 200 members.
The ages of the members are grouped and set out in the table below.

Age (a years)	Frequency
$0 \leqslant a < 10$	8
$10 \leqslant a < 20$	26
$20 \leqslant a < 30$	32
$30 \leqslant a < 40$	45
$40 \leqslant a < 50$	37
$50 \leqslant a < 60$	29
$60 \leqslant a < 70$	16
$70 \leqslant a < 80$	7

(a) Construct a cumulative frequency table.
(b) Draw the cumulative frequency curve.
(c) Work out an estimate of the median.
(d) Work out the interquartile range.
(e) Estimate the percentage of members aged between 35 years and 55 years.

The median age of the members of Russell Golf Club is 42 years. The interquartile range of the members of Russell Golf Club is 33 years.

(f) Compare the distribution of ages of the members of the two golf clubs.

Answer

(a) The cumulative frequency table is

Age	Cumulative frequency
$a < 10$	8
$a < 20$	$8 + 26 = 34$
$a < 30$	$34 + 32 = 66$ (etc)
$a < 40$	111
$a < 50$	148
$a < 60$	177
$a < 70$	193
$a < 80$	200

(b) The cumulative frequency curve is:

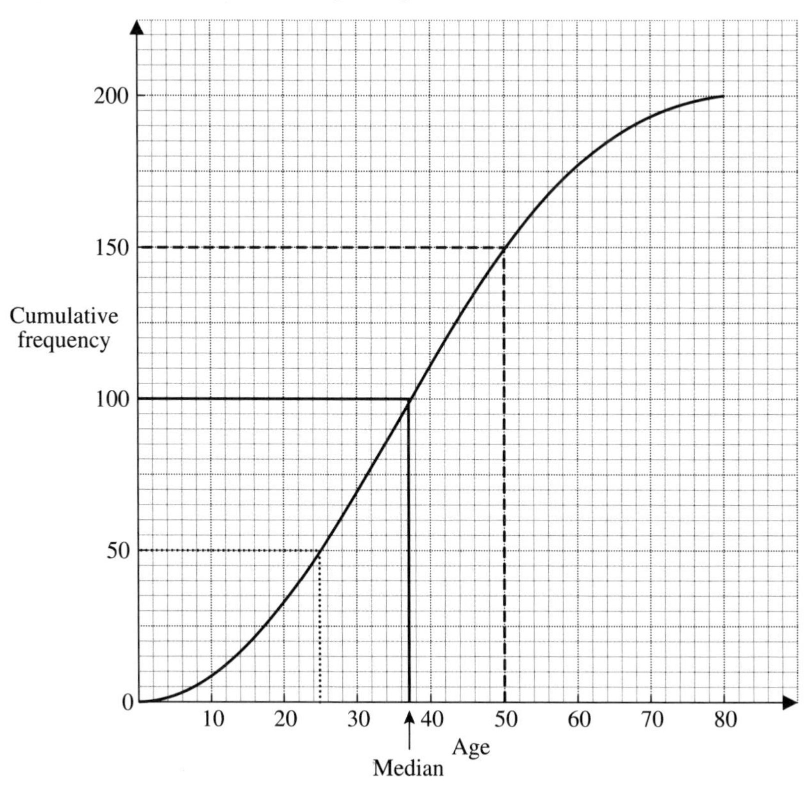

Plot the cumulative frequencies against the upper class boundaries.

(c) Using **1** the median is found from the solid lines on the graph. The estimated median = 37 years

(d) Using **2** the lower quartile is found from the dotted lines on the graph.
The estimated lower quartile = 25 years
Using **3** the upper quartile is found from the dashed lines on the graph.
The estimated upper quartile = 50 years
Using **4**

interquartile range = 50 − 25 = 25 years

(e) Using **5** on a new copy of the cumulative frequency graph, the estimated number of members between 35 years and 55 years is shown by the two dashed lines.

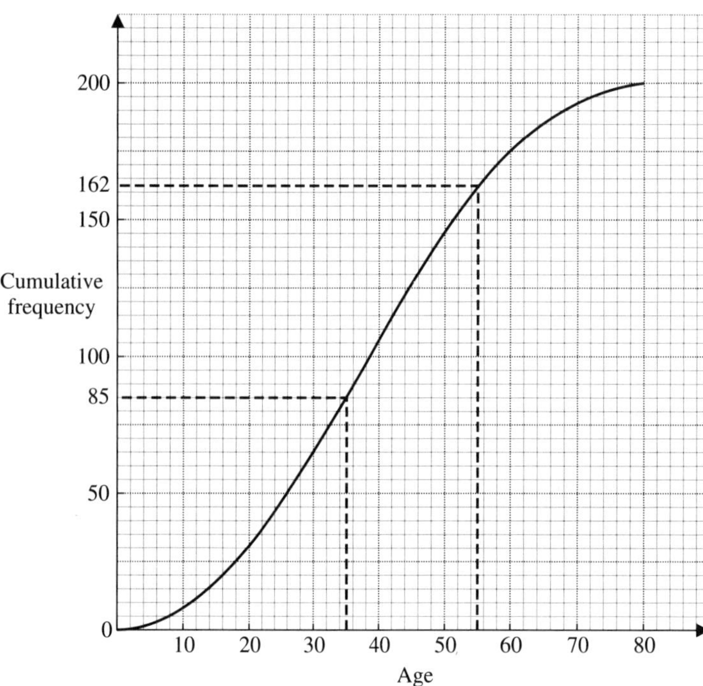

The estimate is

162 − 85 = 77 members

As a percentage, 77 out of 200 is

$$\frac{77}{200} = 38.5\%$$

(f) Using **6**
Comparing the medians:

median age for Russell > median age for Lucea

so it might appear that, on the whole, the Lucea members are younger than the Russell members.

However

interquartile range at Russell > interquartile range at Lucea

This means that the ages of members at Russell are more widely spread than at Lucea. So there could be many members at Russell who are much younger than the members at Lucea.

Revision exercise 22

1 The grouped frequency table gives information about the weekly rainfall (d) in millimetres at Heathrow Airport in 1995.

Weekly rainfall (d) in mm	Number of weeks
$0 \leqslant d < 10$	20
$10 \leqslant d < 20$	18
$20 \leqslant d < 30$	6
$30 \leqslant d < 40$	4
$40 \leqslant d < 50$	2
$50 \leqslant d < 60$	2

(a) Construct a cumulative frequency table.
(b) Draw the cumulative frequency curve.
(c) Estimate the median weekly rainfall.
(d) Estimate the interquartile range for the rainfall.
(e) Estimate the number of weeks in which the rainfall was less than 15 mm. [L]

2 The table gives information about the weights of 100 newborn babies.

Weight (w) in kg	Frequency
$1.0 \leqslant w < 1.5$	4
$1.5 \leqslant w < 2.0$	9
$2.0 \leqslant w < 2.5$	11
$2.5 \leqslant w < 3.0$	21
$3.0 \leqslant w < 3.5$	26
$3.5 \leqslant w < 4.0$	18
$4.0 \leqslant w < 4.5$	9
$4.5 \leqslant w < 5.0$	2

(a) Construct a cumulative frequency table.
(b) Draw a cumulative frequency graph for your table.
(c) Use your cumulative frequency diagram to estimate the median weight, in kilograms, of the newborn babies. Show your method clearly.
(d) Work out an estimate for the interquartile range of the weights of the newborn babies.
(e) Estimate the percentage of babies born with a weight between 2.2 kg and 3.6 kg. [L]

3 The grouped frequency table shows the distribution of the amounts of daily sunshine, in hours, in Downtown in August 1997.

(a) Construct a cumulative frequency table.
(b) Draw the cumulative frequency graph.
(c) Use your cumulative frequency graph to find an estimate for the median amount of daily sunshine, in hours, in August 1997.
Make your method clear.
(d) Estimate the interquartile range for the hours of sunshine in Downtown in August 1997.

Amounts (s) of daily sunshine in hours	Number of days in this class interval
$0 \leqslant s < 2$	2
$2 \leqslant s < 4$	1
$4 \leqslant s < 6$	3
$6 \leqslant s < 8$	8
$8 \leqslant s < 10$	11
$10 \leqslant s < 12$	4
$12 \leqslant s < 14$	2

In Ashwell during August 1997, the median number of hours of daily sunshine was 10.2 hours and the interquartile range was 3 hours.

(e) Compare the distributions of hours of daily sunshine in Downtown and Ashwell for August 1997.

4 A large company is considering paying travelling expenses to its employees who work extra days. To find out much it is likely to cost the company, a survey was carried out on costs of travel. The results are analysed below.

Cost of travel to and from work	
£1 or less	10 employees
more than £1 but no more than £2	20 employees
more than £2 but no more than £3	35 employees
more than £3 but no more than £4	25 employees
more than £4 but no more than £5	8 employees
more than £5 but no more than £6	2 employees
more than £6	0 employees
	100

(a) Copy and complete the cumulative frequency table opposite.
(b) Draw the cumulative frequency curve.
(c) Use your graph to estimate
(i) the median cost of travel
(ii) the lower quartile cost of travel
(iii) the upper quartile cost of travel
(iv) the percentage of employees who spent more than £3.70 on their travel. [L]

Cost, £ c, of travel	Cumulative frequency
$c \leqslant 1$	
$c \leqslant 2$	
$c \leqslant 3$	
$c \leqslant 4$	
$c \leqslant 5$	
$c \leqslant 6$	

Test yourself

What to review

1 The table shows the battery life, t minutes, of a sample of 80 Omega batteries.

If your answer is incorrect:

Battery life (in minutes)	Number of batteries (frequency)
$t < 280$	0
$280 \leqslant t < 290$	5
$290 \leqslant t < 300$	9
$300 \leqslant t < 310$	10
$310 \leqslant t < 320$	15
$320 \leqslant t < 330$	17
$330 \leqslant t < 340$	12
$340 \leqslant t < 350$	8
$350 \leqslant t < 360$	4

(a) Form a cumulative frequency table.

Review Higher book Unit 4, page 74, Section 4.8.

(b) Draw the cumulative frequency curve.

Review Higher book Unit 4, pages 75–9.

(c) Estimate the median battery life.

Review Higher book Unit 15, page 277.

(d) Estimate the interquartile range of the battery lives.

Review Higher book Unit 15, pages 278–80.

A shop owner buys a box of 720 Omega batteries.

(e) Use your graph to estimate how many of these batteries will have a battery life of between 315 and 345 minutes. Show your method clearly. [L]

Review Higher book Unit 15, page 277, Section 15.5.

Answers to Test yourself

1 (a)

Battery life	Cumulative frequency
$t < 280$	0
$t < 290$	5
$t < 300$	14
$t < 310$	24
$t < 320$	39
$t < 330$	56
$t < 340$	68
$t < 350$	76
$t < 360$	80

(c) Just over 320 h **(d)** About 27 h **(e)** Approx. 365

(b)

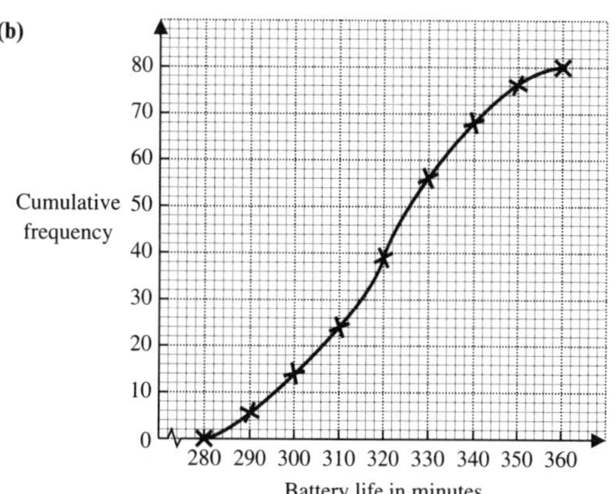

23 Histograms and dispersion

A histogram is a way of representing data from a frequency table. The spread – or dispersion – of a set of data can be measured using the standard deviation.

Key points to remember

1 A histogram can be drawn for equal class intervals.

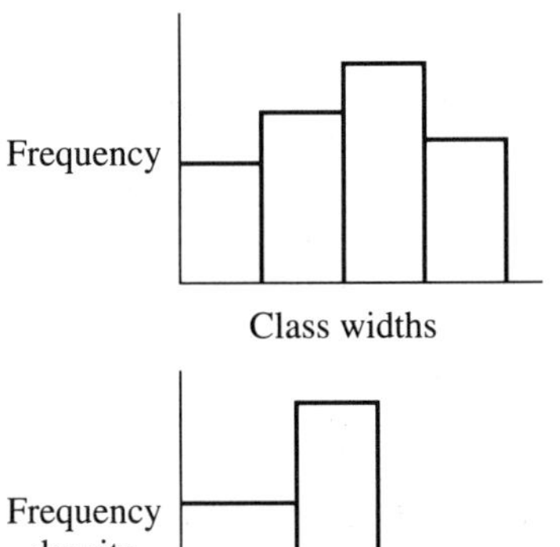

2 A histogram can be drawn for unequal class intervals.

3 When unequal class intervals are used the vertical axis is frequency density.

4 $\text{Frequency density} = \dfrac{\text{frequency}}{\text{class width}}$

5 For any histogram the areas of the rectangles are proportional to the frequencies they represent.

6 The standard deviation of a set of data is a measure of its spread or dispersion. It can be written in the following ways:

$$\text{standard deviation} = \sqrt{\frac{\Sigma(x-\overline{x})^2}{n}}$$

$$\text{standard deviation} = \sqrt{\frac{\Sigma(x^2)}{n} - \overline{x}^2}$$

$$\text{standard deviation} = \sqrt{\frac{\Sigma(x^2)}{n} - \left(\frac{\Sigma x}{n}\right)^2}$$

7 If the mean and standard deviation of $(x_1, x_2, \ldots, x_n)$ are $\overline{x}$ and s then the mean and standard deviation of $(ax_1 + b, ax_2 + b, \ldots, ax_n + b)$ are mean $= a\overline{x} + b$, standard deviation $= as$

Example 1

A sack contains 108 potatoes.
The frequency table gives information about the masses of these potatoes.

Mass (m) grams	Frequency
$0 < m \leqslant 100$	7
$100 < m \leqslant 150$	26
$150 < m \leqslant 200$	30
$200 < m \leqslant 250$	35
$250 < m \leqslant 400$	10

Use the information to draw the histogram for this distribution.

Answer

Using **3** and **4** work out the frequency density using

$$\text{frequency density} = \frac{\text{frequency}}{\text{class width}}$$

Mass	Frequency	Class width	Frequency density
0 to 100	7	100	$7 \div 100 = 0.07$
100 to 150	26	50	$26 \div 50 = 0.52$
150 to 200	30	50	$30 \div 50 = 0.6$
200 to 250	35	50	$35 \div 50 = 0.7$
250 to 400	12	150	$12 \div 150 = 0.08$

Now draw the histogram, using **2** and **4**

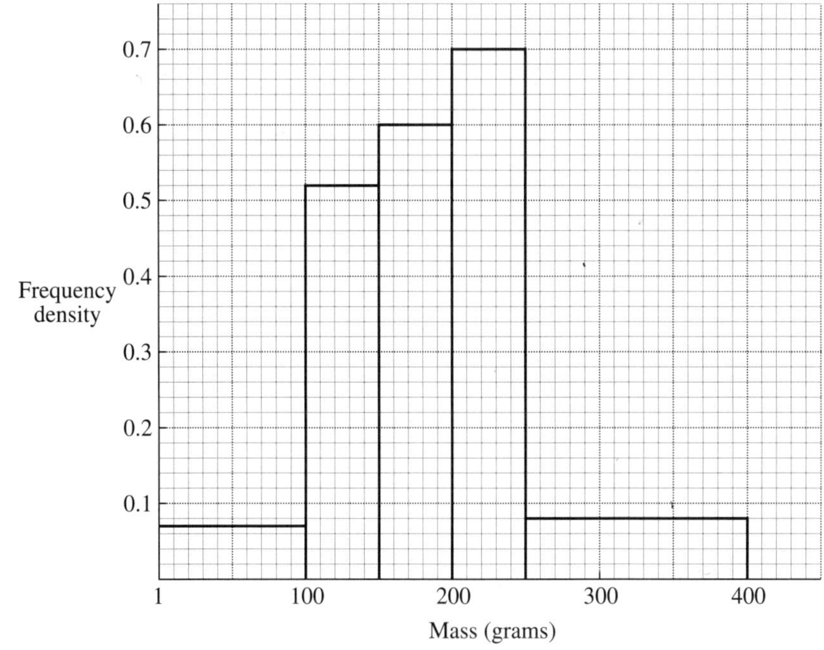

Worked examination question 1 [L]

The histogram gives information about the ages of the teachers at a school on 1st September last year.

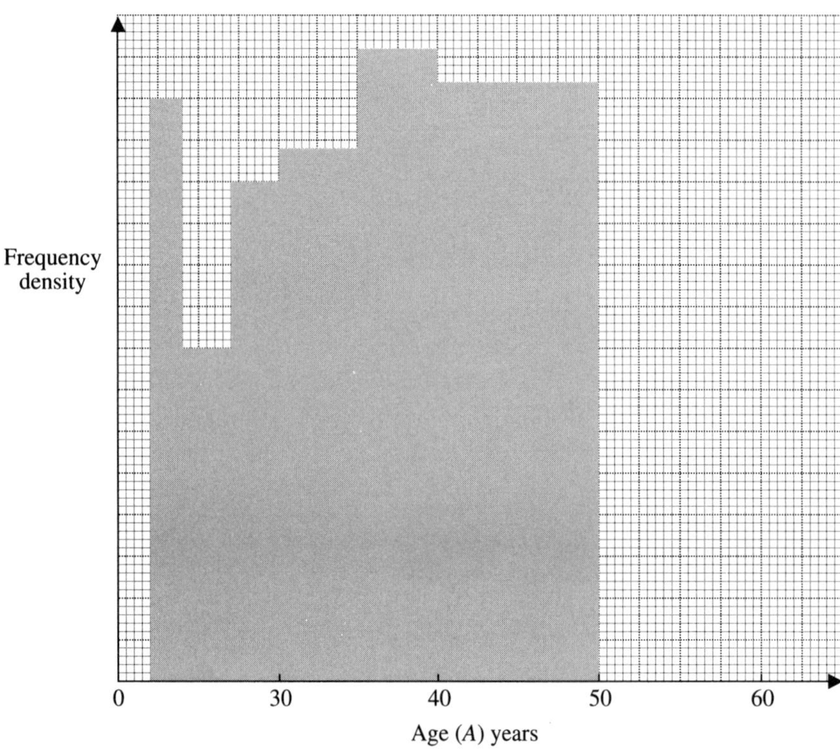

(a) Use the information in the histogram to complete the frequency table.

Age (A) years	Frequency
$22 \leqslant A < 24$	
$24 \leqslant A < 27$	
$27 \leqslant A < 30$	
$30 \leqslant A < 35$	16
$35 \leqslant A < 40$	19
$40 \leqslant A < 50$	
$50 \leqslant A < 65$	27

(b) Use the information in the frequency table to complete the histogram.

Answer

(a) For the 30 to 35 age group, using **4**

$$\text{frequency density} = \frac{\text{frequency}}{\text{class width}} = \frac{16}{5} = 3.2$$

So, on the grid, 64 squares represent 3.2 units
$\therefore$ 20 squares represent 1 unit

So the scale for the frequency density axis is as shown, right.

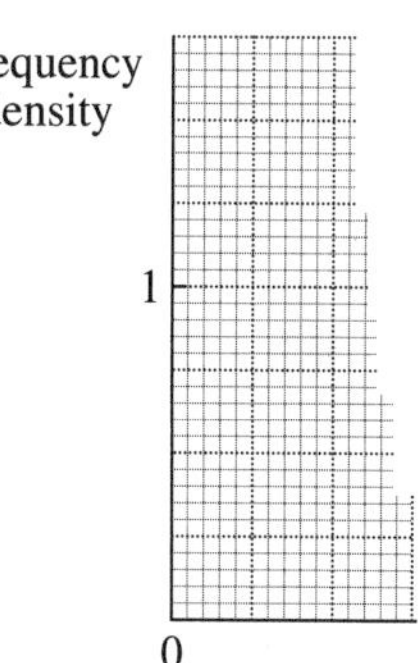

Now work out the frequency densities (heights of bars) for each age range using **4** again:

frequency = frequency density × class width

Age range	Frequency density	Class width	Frequency
22 to 24	3.5	2	7
24 to 27	2	3	6
27 to 30	3	3	9
30 to 35	3.2	5	16
35 to 40	3.8	5	19
40 to 50	3.6	10	36
50 to 65	$\frac{27}{15} = 1.8$	15	27

(b) Using **5** the completed histogram is:

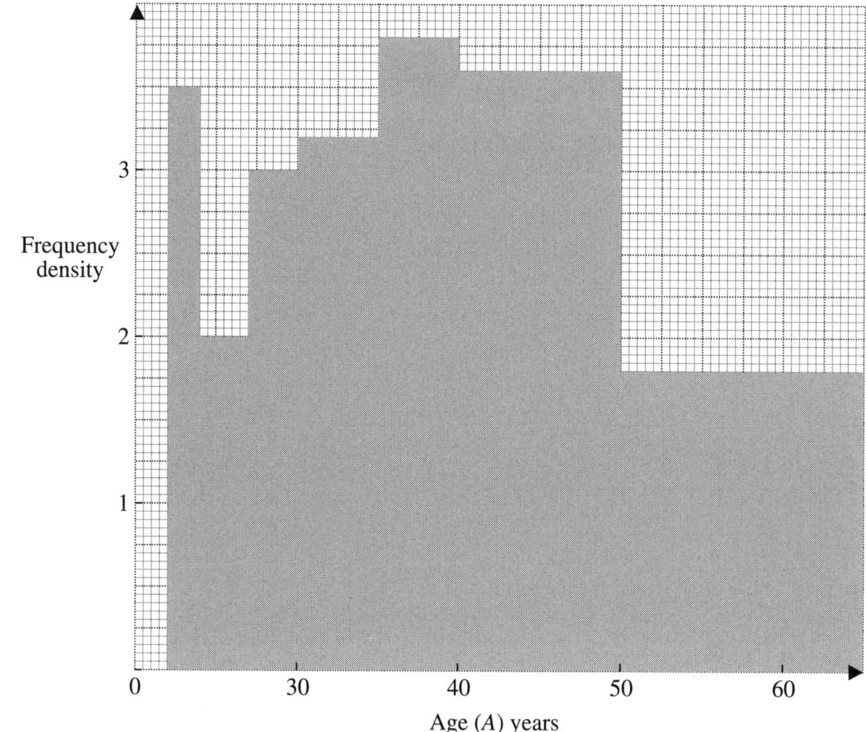

Example 2

Calculate the standard deviation of the 6 numbers:

3, 7, 8, 12, 6, 9

Answer

Using **6**

$$\Sigma x = 3 + 7 + 8 + 12 + 6 + 9 = 45$$

So $\bar{x} = \dfrac{\Sigma x}{n} = \dfrac{45}{6} = 7.5$

and $\left(\dfrac{\Sigma x}{n}\right)^2 = 7.5^2 = 56.25$

Also $\Sigma x^2 = 3^2 + 7^2 + 8^2 + 12^2 + 6^2 + 9^2$
$= 9 + 49 + 64 + 144 + 36 + 81 = 383$

So $\dfrac{\Sigma x^2}{n} = \dfrac{383}{6} = 63.83$

standard deviation $= \sqrt{\dfrac{\Sigma x^2}{n} - \left(\dfrac{\Sigma x}{n}\right)^2} = \sqrt{63.83 - 56.25} = 2.75$

Example 3

Twelve students took a test marked out of 16. Their raw marks are given in the table below:

Raw mark	12	13	14	15	16
Frequency	2	3	1	4	2

(a) Calculate the mean and standard deviation of the marks.

The teacher changes the raw marks to final marks out of 100 using the formula:

final mark $= 6 \times$ raw mark $+ 4$

(b) Calculate the mean and standard deviation of the final marks.

Answer

(a) mean $= \dfrac{\Sigma fx}{\Sigma f}$

$$= \frac{(12 \times 2) + (13 \times 3) + (14 \times 1) + (15 \times 4) + (16 \times 2)}{12}$$

$$\bar{x} = \frac{169}{12} = 14.08 \text{ (2 d.p.)}$$

Using **6**, standard deviation $= \sqrt{\dfrac{\Sigma(x^2)}{n} - \bar{x}^2}$

x	12	13	14	15	16
x^2	144	169	196	225	256
Frequency	2	3	1	4	2

$\Sigma x^2 = (144 \times 2) + (169 \times 3) + (196 \times 1) + (225 \times 4) + (256 \times 2) = 2403$

So $\qquad$ standard deviation $= \sqrt{\frac{2403}{12} - 14.08^2} = 1.382$

(b) Using **7**

mean final mark $= 6 \times$ mean raw mark $+ 4$
$= 6 \times 14.08 + 4 = 88.5$ (1 d.p.)
standard deviation of final mark $= 6 \times$ standard deviation of raw mark
$= 6 \times 1.382 = 8.29$ (2 d.p.)

Revision exercise 23

1 The waiting time for patients to be seen by a doctor after arriving at the accident department of a hospital during a weekend period were recorded. The histogram shows the results.

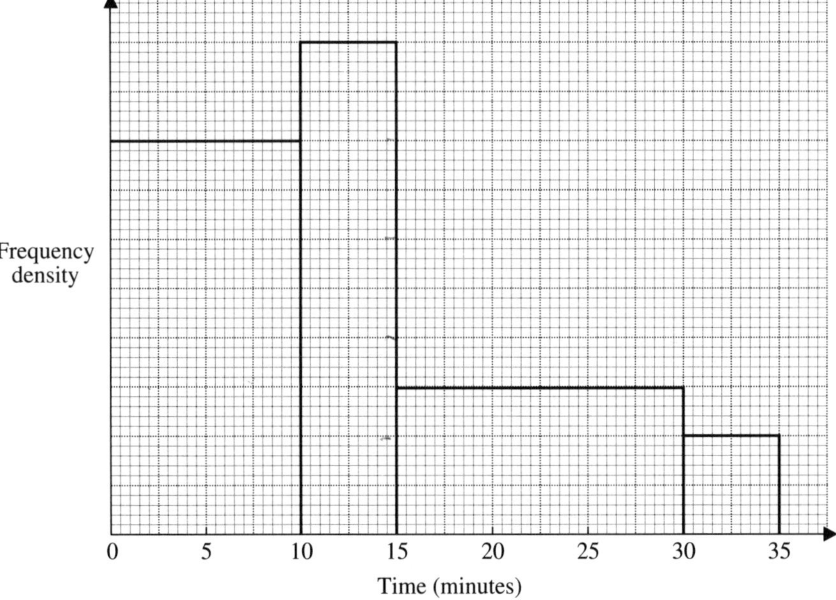

There were exactly 20 patients who were seen by a doctor in a time which was greater than or equal to 10 minutes and less than 15 minutes.

No patient had to wait 35 minutes or longer before being seen by a doctor.

Use the information in the histogram to complete the frequency table.

Waiting time in minutes (t)	Frequency
$0 \leqslant t < 10$	
$10 \leqslant t < 15$	20
$15 \leqslant t < 30$	
$30 \leqslant t < 35$	
$35 \leqslant t$	0

[L]

2 The mean and standard deviation of the mass of coffee in 10 jars of Nicer coffee are:

mean mass = 210.4 g, standard deviation = 7.64 g

The masses of coffee in 10 jars of Brand coffee measured to the nearest gram are:

218, 222, 206, 212, 220, 200, 196, 222, 194, 212

(a) Calculate the mean and standard deviation of the mass of coffee in the 10 jars of Brand coffee.

(b) Comment on the similarity or difference of the distribution of the mass of coffee in the two brands.

3 Jenny writes 8 essays for her GCSE English.
The marks out of 20 she scores on these essays are:

12, 15, 13, 17, 10, 9, 15, 13

(a) Work out the standard deviation of these marks.

Jenny's teacher converts each of these marks to a percentage.

(b) Work out the standard deviation of these percentages.

4 Show that the standard deviation of any seven consecutive whole numbers is 2.

5 The table shows the working life (h) in hours of 120 overhead projector bulbs.

Number of hours (h)	Frequency
$0 \leqslant h < 20$	10
$20 \leqslant h < 30$	20
$30 \leqslant h < 40$	50
$40 \leqslant h < 60$	30
$60 \leqslant h < 100$	10

(a) Work out the number of bulbs represented by the square shown as the key.

(b) Copy and complete the histogram to show the information in the table.

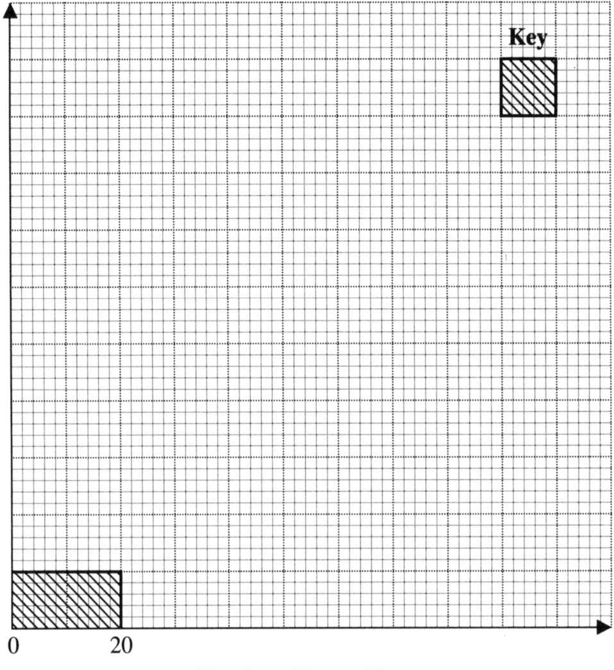

6 George writes 20 letters.
The number of spelling mistakes he makes in these letters are recorded below.

Number of spelling mistakes	1	2	3	4	5
Number of letters	6	2	5	5	2

Calculate the standard deviation of the number of spelling mistakes.

7 There are 200 members of Lucea Golf Club.
The distribution of their ages (A) is shown in the table below.

Age (A) years	Frequency
$0 \leqslant A < 20$	15
$20 \leqslant A < 30$	35
$30 \leqslant A < 40$	58
$40 \leqslant A < 50$	52
$50 \leqslant A < 60$	20
$60 \leqslant A < 65$	12
$65 \leqslant A < 90$	8

Draw a histogram to represent the information in the table.

Test yourself

What to review

1 In a survey on October 1st, pupils at Lucea High school were asked how long they had taken to go from home to school that morning. Each pupil present ticked one and only one of the following responses.

Time in minutes t	
$0 \leqslant t < 5$	
$5 \leqslant t < 15$	
$15 \leqslant t < 25$	
$25 \leqslant t < 40$	
$40 \leqslant t < 70$	
$t \geqslant 70$	

Exactly 96 pupils ticked the '$5 \leqslant t < 15$' box. No pupil ticked the '$t \geqslant 70$' box.

If your answer is incorrect:

The histogram shows the results of the survey.

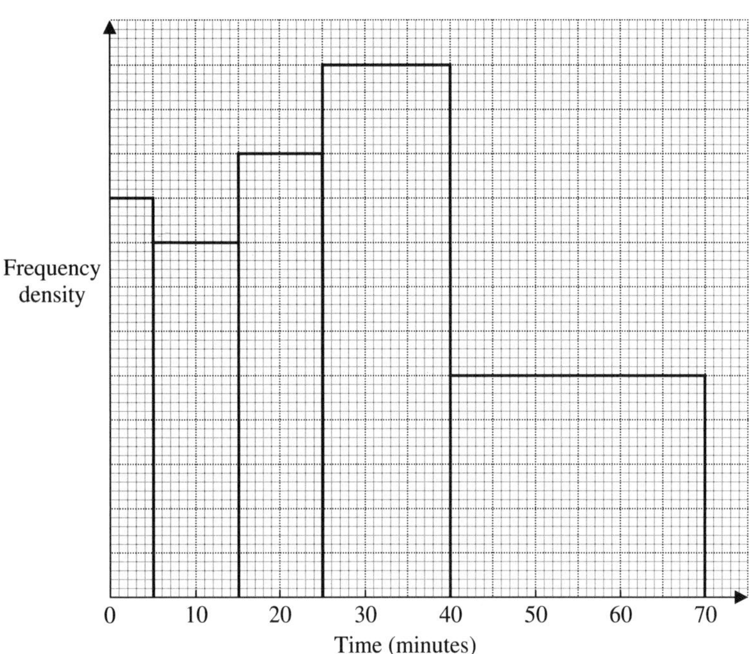

Calculate the number of pupils who were absent on October 1st given that the total number of pupils at the school is 726. [L]

Review Higher book Unit 29, page 534, Section 29.2.

---

2 The raw marks obtained by 6 students in a History Examination are:

29, 31, 40, 41, 49, 50

(a) Calculate the standard deviation of these raw marks.

Review Higher book Unit 29, page 548,Example 7.

The final mark for each student is found by the formula

final mark $= 0.4 \times$ raw mark

(b) Work out the standard deviation of the final marks.

Review Higher book Unit 29, page 549, Example 8.

Answers to Test yourself

1 60 **2** **(a)** 8 **(b)** 3.2

24 Probability

Probability is a measure of the likelihood – or chance – of something happening.

Key points to remember

1 $\text{P(event)} = \dfrac{\text{the number of ways the event can occur}}{\text{the total number of possibilities}}$

2 $\text{Relative frequency} = \dfrac{\text{number of times event occurs}}{\text{total number of trials}}$

3 Probabilities should only be expressed as fractions, decimals or percentages.

4 When an event has several separate and mutually exclusive outcomes then the sum of the probabilities of all these outcomes is 1. For example:
if an event has 3 outcomes, A, B, C then

$$\text{P}(A) + \text{P}(B) + \text{P}(C) = 1$$

Mutually exclusive means that no two outcomes can occur at the same time.

5 For mutually exclusive events:

$$\text{P}(A \text{ or } B) = \text{P}(A) + \text{P}(B)$$

6 Event A and event 'not A' are mutually exclusive and cover all possibilities and so

$$\text{P(not } A) = 1 - \text{P}(A)$$

7 For independent events:

$$\text{P}(A \text{ and } B) = \text{P}(A) \times \text{P}(B)$$

Independent means that the outcome of the event does not affect the outcome of the other.

8 In some cases the probability of a second outcome, or event, will be dependent on a previous outcome. In such cases the second probability is conditional.

9 In all cases you should know how to set up and use tree diagrams.

Example 1

There are three candidates for an election. Their names are: Abbot, Bailey and Cassell.

Before the election a survey of the voting intentions of 200 people, chosen at random, is conducted.

The results of the survey are:

Candidate	Number of likely voters
Abbot	120
Bailey	48
Cassell	32

(a) Use this information to work out an estimate of the probability that a randomly chosen voter will vote for Bailey.

On the day of the election exactly 25 000 votes are cast.

(b) Estimate, with reasons, the number of votes likely to be cast for Abbot.

On the day of the election, two voters are chosen at random.

(c) Estimate the probability that:
 (i) they will both vote for Cassell.
 (ii) at least one of them will vote for Cassell.

Answer

(a) Using **2** the estimated probability, P(Bailey) or P(B), is:

$$P(B) = \frac{\text{number of likely voters for Bailey}}{\text{total number in survey}}$$

$$P(B) = \frac{48}{200} = 0.24$$

(b) Using **2** $P(\text{Abbot}) = P(A) = \frac{120}{200} = 0.6$

Using **1** the estimate for the likely number of votes cast for Abott is given by:

$$P(A) = \frac{\text{likely number of votes for Abbot}}{\text{total votes cast}}$$

Rearranging:

$$\text{likely number of votes for Abbot} = P(A) \times \text{ total votes cast}$$

So $\quad \text{likely number of votes for Abbot} = 0.6 \times 25\,000$

$$= 15\,000$$

(c) Using **2**

$$\text{P(Cassell)} = \text{P}(C) = \frac{32}{200} = 0.16$$

(i) Using **7**

$$\begin{aligned}\text{P}(C \text{ and } C) &= 0.16 \times 0.16 \\ &= 0.0256\end{aligned}$$

(ii) Using **6**

$$\text{P(at least 1 votes for } C) = 1 - \text{P(both do not vote for } C)$$

Using **6** again,

$$\begin{aligned}\text{P(not voting for } C) &= 1 - \text{P}(C) \\ &= 1 - 0.16 \\ &= 0.84\end{aligned}$$

Now using **7**

$$\begin{aligned}\text{P(not } C \text{ and not } C) &= 0.84 \times 0.84 \\ &= 0.7056\end{aligned}$$

So
$$\begin{aligned}\text{P(at least 1 votes for } C) &= 1 - 0.7056 \\ &= 0.2944\end{aligned}$$

Worked examination question [L]

A bag contains 15 equal sized coloured balls.
6 balls are red, 4 balls are blue and the remaining balls are white.

A ball is selected at random.
(a) Write down the probability that this ball will be white.

A ball is selected at random and its colour recorded.
This ball is not put back in the bag.
A second ball is then selected and its colour recorded.
This ball is also not put back in the bag.

(b) Draw a probability tree diagram.

(c) Using your tree diagram or otherwise, work out the probabilities of
 (i) both recorded colours being blue
 (ii) both recorded colours being the same.

A third ball is then selected at random and its colour recorded.
(d) Work out the probability of at least two of the recorded colours being red.

Answer

(a) Using **1**

$$P(W) = \frac{5}{15} = \frac{1}{3}$$

(b) Using **9** with **8** and **4**, set up the tree diagram as follows:

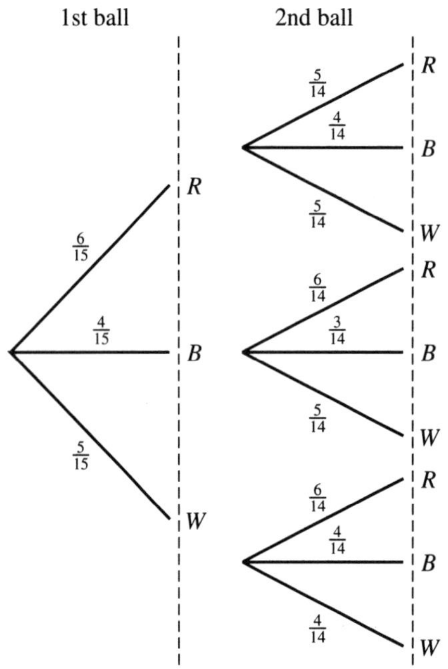

(c) (i) Using **7** and the tree diagram

$$P(B \text{ and } B) = \frac{4}{15} \times \frac{3}{14} = \frac{12}{210} = \frac{2}{35}$$

(ii) Using **5** and **7** again

$$\begin{aligned} P(\text{both same}) &= P(RR) + P(BB) + P(WW) \\ &= \frac{6}{15} \times \frac{5}{14} + \frac{4}{15} \times \frac{3}{14} + \frac{5}{15} \times \frac{4}{14} \\ &= \frac{30}{210} + \frac{12}{210} + \frac{20}{210} \\ &= \frac{62}{210} = \frac{31}{105} \end{aligned}$$

(d) Extend the appropriate parts of the tree diagram to cover all cases with at least two red:

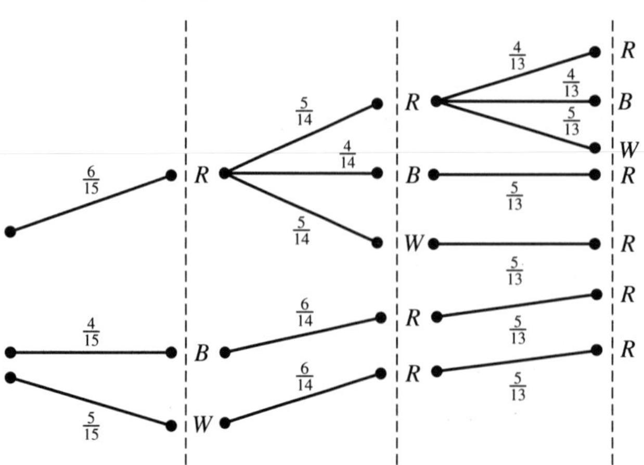

Using **7** probability of at least two red is:

$$\left(\tfrac{6}{15}\times\tfrac{5}{14}\times\tfrac{4}{13}\right)+\left(\tfrac{6}{15}\times\tfrac{5}{14}\times\tfrac{4}{13}\right)+\left(\tfrac{6}{15}\times\tfrac{5}{14}\times\tfrac{5}{13}\right)+\left(\tfrac{6}{15}\times\tfrac{4}{14}\times\tfrac{5}{13}\right)+\left(\tfrac{6}{15}\times\tfrac{5}{14}\times\tfrac{5}{13}\right)$$
$$+\left(\tfrac{4}{15}\times\tfrac{6}{14}\times\tfrac{5}{13}\right)+\left(\tfrac{5}{15}\times\tfrac{6}{14}\times\tfrac{5}{13}\right)$$

Note, the top row is:

$$\left(\tfrac{6}{15}\times\tfrac{5}{14}\right)\times\left(\tfrac{4}{13}+\tfrac{4}{13}+\tfrac{5}{13}\right)=\tfrac{6}{15}\times\tfrac{5}{14}\times 1=\tfrac{30}{210}$$

So $$\text{P(at least 2 red)}=\tfrac{30}{210}+\tfrac{120}{2730}+\tfrac{150}{2730}+\tfrac{120}{2730}+\tfrac{150}{2730}$$

$$=\frac{390+120+150+120+150}{2730}$$

$$=\frac{930}{2730}$$

$$\text{P(at least 2 red)}=\tfrac{31}{91}$$

Revision exercise 24

1 Peter and Asif are both taking their driving test for a motorcycle for the first time.

The table below gives the probabilities that they will pass the test at the first attempt or, if they fail the first time, the probability that they will pass at the next attempt.

	Probability of passing at first attempt	**Probability of passing at next attempt if they fail the first attempt**
Peter	0.5	0.8
Asif	0.8	0.9

On a particular day 2000 people will take the test for the first time.

For each person the probability that they will pass the test at the first attempt is the same as the probability that Asif will pass the test at the first attempt.

(a) Work out an estimate for how many of these 2000 people are likely to pass the test at the first attempt.

(b) Calculate the probability that both Peter and Asif will pass the test at the first attempt.

(c) Calculate the probability that Peter will pass the test at the first attempt and Asif will fail the test at the first attempt.

(d) Calculate the probability that Asif will pass the test within the first two attempts. [L adapted]

2 There are two sets of traffic lights on Paul's route to school.

The probability that the first set of lights will be green is $\frac{3}{5}$.
If he finds the first set of lights green, the probability that the second set of lights will be green, when he gets to them, is $\frac{2}{7}$.
If he finds the first set of lights are not green, the probability that the second set of lights will be green, when he gets to them, is $\frac{4}{7}$.

(a) Draw a tree diagram for this situation.
(b) Calculate the probability that Paul will find the first set of lights is not green and the second set of lights is green.
(c) Calculate the probability that Paul will find the second set of lights is green.

3 A bag contains 12 equal sized coloured balls. 7 of the balls are red, 2 are blue and 3 are green.

A ball is selected, at random, from the bag, and then replaced.
Another ball is then selected.
Work out the probability of both balls being the same colour.

4 Heather has five red scarves, four white scarves and three blue scarves.
She chooses a scarf at random to wear at work.

Bavines has six red scarves and four white scarves.
She also chooses a scarf at random to wear at work.

Calculate the probability that Heather and Bavines will wear the same colour scarf to work tomorrow. [L}

5 At a Lucky Dip stall at a fair, there are 20 identical tins in a sack. 16 tins contain baked beans and 4 tins contain salmon. Declan takes 2 tins at random from the sack.

(a) What is the probability that the first tin will contain baked beans?
(b) If the first tin contains baked beans, what is the probability that the second tin will also contain baked beans?
(c) Find the probability that Declan will get
   (i) two tins of baked beans
   (ii) one tin of baked beans and one tin of salmon. [L]

6 A box contains 12 chocolates. 5 are milk, 4 are plain and 3 are white chocolate.
June, George and Salim each choose a chocolate at random and eat it.
Work out the probability that the 3 chocolates will be of the same type.

Test yourself

What to review

1 A bag contains some red, some white and some blue counters.
A counter is picked at random.
The probability that it will be red is 0.2.
The probability that it will be white is 0.3.

If your answer is incorrect:

(a) What is the probability that a counter picked at random will be either red or white?

Review Higher book Unit 9, page 176, Example 3.

(b) What is the probability that a counter picked at random will be either red or blue?

Review Higher book Unit 9, page 176, Example 4.

A counter will be picked at random. Its colour will be recorded. The counter will be put back in the bag.

A second counter will be picked at random.
Its colour will be recorded.

(c) By drawing a tree diagram, or otherwise, calculate the probability that the first counter will be red and the second counter will be white.

Review Higher book Unit 9, page 181, Sections 9.5 and 9.6.

(d) Calculate the probability that both counters will be white.

Review Higher book Unit 9, page 181, Sections 9.5 and 9.6.

---

2 Wasim runs a stall in the market. He has 16 shirts to sell.
8 of the shirts are white, 5 of the shirts are blue, and the remaining 3 are red.
Each customer's choice of colour when buying a shirt can be assumed to be made at random.

Mrs Jones goes to Wasim's stall to buy a shirt.
She is followed by Mr Wilkins, who also goes to the stall to buy a shirt.
They will both buy one shirt only.

(a) Work out the probability that Mrs Jones and Mr Wilkins will both buy a white shirt.

Review Higher book Unit 25, page 460, Sections 25.1 and 25.2.

(b) Work out the probability that Mrs Jones and Mr Wilkins will buy shirts of the same colour.

Review Higher book Unit 25, page 460, Sections 25.1 and 25.2.

(c) Work out the probability that Mrs Jones and Mr Wilkins will buy shirts which are of different colours.

Review Higher book Unit 25, page 460, Sections 25.1 and 25.2.

Answers to Test yourself

1 **(a)** 0.5 **(b)** 0.7 **(c)** 0.06 **(d)** 0.09 **2** **(a)** $\frac{7}{30}$ **(b)** $\frac{41}{120}$ **(c)** $\frac{79}{120}$

Examination practice paper

What to review

If your answer is incorrect review:

1 In the 'Sales' a shop reduces all its prices by 20%

(a) Work out the price in the Sales of a coat which had a price of £68 before the Sales. (2 marks) *Unit 2, Key point* **2**

The price of a dress in the Sales is £28.

(b) Work out the price of this dress before the Sales. (2 marks) *Unit 2, Example 3*

2 **(a)** Show that one solution of the equation

$$x^3 - 4x = 30$$

lies in the range $3 < x < 4$

(b) Use a method of trial and improvement to work out this solution of

$$x^3 - 4x = 30$$

correct to one decimal place. (4 marks) *Unit 5, Key point* **5**

3 A survey was carried out to find how minutes late the Express was in June 1997.
The results of the survey are shown in the table below.

Time (t) minutes late	Number of days
$0 < t \leqslant 4$	6
$4 < t \leqslant 8$	8
$8 < t \leqslant 12$	12
$12 < t \leqslant 16$	3
$16 < t \leqslant 20$	1

(a) Work out an estimate for the mean number of minutes the Express was late in June 1997. (4 marks) *Unit 21, Key point* **1**

A day in June was picked at random.

(b) Work out the probability that the Express was 10 or more minutes late on that day. (2 marks) *Unit 24, Key point* **2**

4 Solve the simultaneous equations

$$4x - y = 13$$
$$3x + 2y = 7$$

(3 marks) *Unit 5, Key point* **3**

5

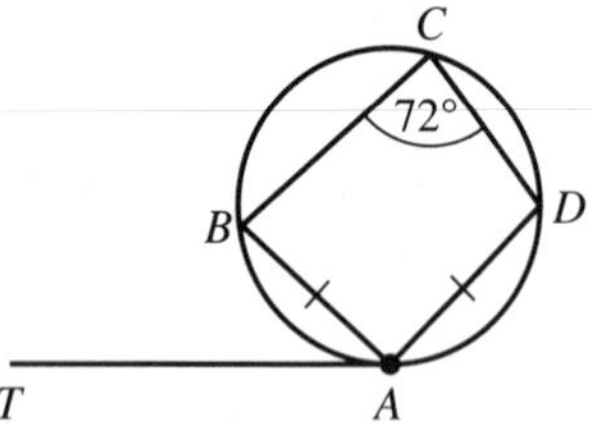

ABC and D lie on the circumference of a circle.
TA is a tangent to the circle at A. $AB = AD$.
Work out, giving your reasons, the angle $T\hat{A}B$. (3 marks) *Unit 19, Key points* **7** *and* **8**

If your answer is incorrect review:

6 A solid metal cylinder has a circular base of diameter 12 cm.
The height of the cylinder is 15 cm.

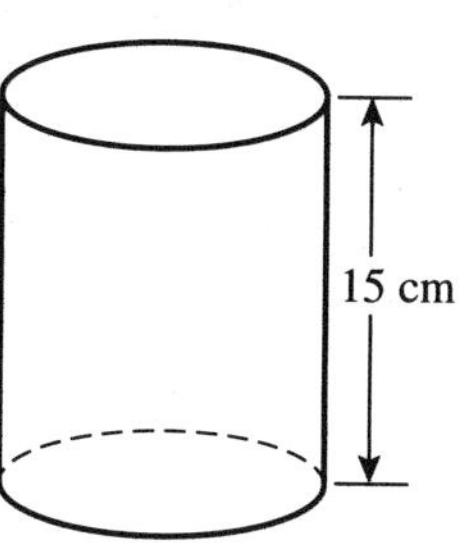

(a) Work out the volume of the cylinder in cm^3
Give your answer correct to two decimal places. (3 marks) — *Unit 17, Key point* **2**

The cylinder is melted down and re-cast as a solid cube of side x cm.

(b) Work out the value of x. (2 marks) — *Unit 17, Worked examination question.*

7 (a) Factorize completely:

$$2x^3y + 6xy^3$$

(2 marks) — *Unit 1, Key point* **10**

(b) Solve the equation:

$$\frac{7 + 2x}{x} = -3$$

(3 marks) — *Unit 5, Example 2*

(c) **(i)** Factorize $x^2 - 3x - 28$
(ii) Hence or otherwise, solve the equation
$x^2 - 3x - 28 = 0$ (4 marks) — *Unit 1, Key point* **11**, *and Unit 6.*

8 In the newspaper, 150 cars are advertised for sale.
The distribution of the prices of these cars is given in the table below.

Price (P) £s	Number of cars
$0 < P \leqslant 1000$	4
$1000 < P \leqslant 2000$	9
$2000 < P \leqslant 3000$	14
$3000 < P \leqslant 4000$	21
$4000 < P \leqslant 5000$	36
$5000 < P \leqslant 6000$	22
$6000 < P \leqslant 7000$	17
$7000 < P \leqslant 8000$	14
$8000 < P \leqslant 9000$	8
$9000 < P \leqslant 10\,000$	5

(a) Draw a cumulative frequency curve for this distribution.
(3 marks) — *Unit 22, Example 1.*

(b) Use your curve to obtain estimates for:
(i) the median price
(ii) the interquartile range of the prices (5 marks) — *Unit 22, Key points* **1**, *and* **4**

If your answer is incorrect review:

9 $VABC$ is a tetrahedron.
The vertex V is vertically above B.
The horizontal base is the triangle ABC.
$AB = 7$ cm, $BC = 15$ cm and $VC = 17$ cm.
The angles ABC, VBA and VBC are all right angles.

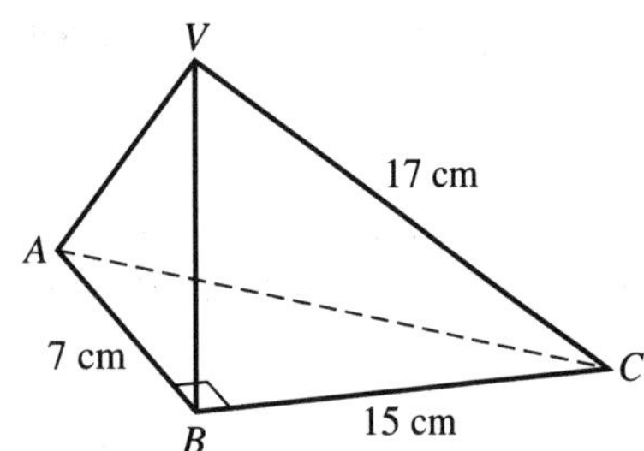

(a) Work out the lengths of
(i) AC **(ii)** VB (3 marks) *Unit 12, Key point* **2**

(b) Work out the angle AVB. (3 marks) *Unit 12, Key point* **3**

(c) Work out the volume of $VABC$. (2 marks) *Unit 17, Key point* **3**

10 There are approximately 37 500 families living in Lucea.
(a) Write the number 37 500 in standard form (2 marks) *Unit 2, Key point* **8**

The average number of people living in each family in Lucea is 4.4.
(b) Work out an estimate for the number of people living in Lucea.
Give your answer in standard form. (2 marks) *Unit 2, Key point* **8**

11 A bag contains 16 equal sized coloured balls.
8 of the balls are white
5 of the balls are red.
3 of the balls are green.

A ball is selected at random from the bag and its colour recorded.
This ball is not put back in the bag.
A second ball is selected at random from the bag and its colour recorded.

(a) Draw a probability tree diagram for this situation. Label the branches of the tree diagram with the appropriate probabilities. (2 marks) *Unit 24, Key point* **9**

(b) Using your tree diagram or otherwise, work out the probabilities that:
(i) both balls selected will be red
(ii) both balls selected will be of the same colour. (5 marks) *Unit 24, Key point* **7**

If your answer is incorrect review:

12 The diagram represents the path taken by a ship. The ship leaves a harbour, H, and travels 45 km to a marker buoy, B. At B the ship turns on a bearing of 048° and travels a further 32 km to a lighthouse, L.
At L the ship turns again and travels in a straight line back to H.

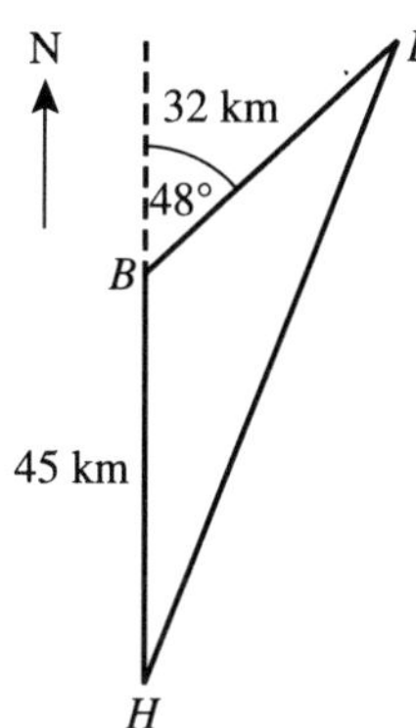

Calculate the total distance travelled by the ship. (4 marks) *Unit 14, Key point* **3**

13 The radius of a sphere is r cm.
The volume, in cm^3, of this sphere is numerically equal to the diameter, in cm, of the sphere.

Show that $r = \sqrt{\dfrac{3}{2\pi}}$ (4 marks) *Unit 17, Key point* **4**

14 p is a whole number.
n is a positive integer.

(a) State clearly the condition on n which will make $p + \sqrt{n}$ irrational. (1 mark) *Unit 3, Key point* **4**

(b) Show that the difference between two irrational numbers can be rational. (3 marks) *Unit 3, Key points* **3** *and* **4**

15 Find an expression in x for the standard deviation of

$$5, \quad 5, \quad 7, \quad 8, \quad 5x$$

(You do not need to simplify your expression.) (4 marks) *Unit 23, Key point* **6**

16 The equation of a graph is $y = ax + b$, where a and b are fixed numbers and x and y are variables.
The equation of a second graph is $y = mx + c$, where m and c are fixed numbers.

(a) Show that the x-coordinate of the point of intersection of the two graphs is given by

$$x = \frac{c - b}{a - m}$$

(3 marks) *Unit 5, Key point* **3**

(b) Explain clearly what happens in the case where $a = m$ and $c = b$ (2 marks) *Unit 5, Worked examination question 1*

If your answer is incorrect review:

17 In the diagram

$OC = 3AB$

$\overrightarrow{OA} = \mathbf{a}$ and $\overrightarrow{AB} = \mathbf{b}$

OC is parallel to AB.

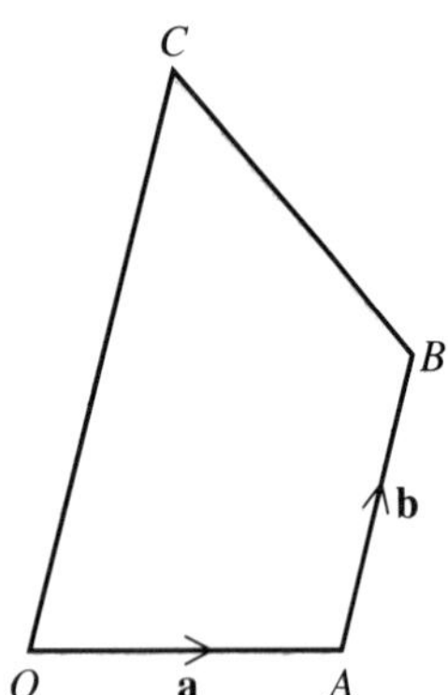

Find expressions in terms of **a** and **b** for each of the vectors

(i) $\overrightarrow{OB}$ **(ii)** $\overrightarrow{BC}$ **(iii)** $\overrightarrow{AC}$ (5 marks) — *Unit 18, Key points* **3**, **5** *and* **6**

18 (a) Factorize $4x^2 - y^2$

(b) Given that $4x^2 - y^2 = 35$ and that $2x + y = 7$ find the values of x and y. (5 marks) — *Unit 1, Key point* **12**

19 s is inversely proportional to t^2.
When $t = 2$, $s = 25$.

Find the value of s when $t = 5$. (3 marks) — *Unit 8, Key point* **6**

20 The equation of a curve is

$$y = x^2 - 6x + 11$$

Find the coordinates of the point on the curve for which y has a minimum value. (5 marks) — *Unit 9, Key point* **2**

Answers

Revision exercise 1

1 **(a)** 8 **(b)** $\frac{1}{3}$

2 **(a)** 1 **(b)** $\frac{1}{8}$

3 **(a)** 5 **(b)** $\frac{1}{2}$ **(c)** $4\frac{1}{2}$

4 **(a)** $5x(2x-1)$ **(b)** $3\frac{1}{2}$

5 **(a)** $3x^2y^2(2-x^2)$ **(b)** $4xy(3y^2-2x^3)$

6 $(x+y)(a-b)$

7 **(a)** a^9 **(b)** x^6 **(c)** $12x^5$ **(d)** x^4
(e) $3x^3$ **(f)** $\pm\frac{1}{4}$ **(g)** 32 **(h)** 1024 **(i)** 9

8 **(a)** $\dfrac{2x+y}{xy}$ **(b)** $\dfrac{13}{6x}$ **(c)** $\dfrac{2x}{3}$ **(d)** $\dfrac{-9-3x}{(x+2)(x-1)}$

9 **(a)** $x(x+4)$ **(b)** $2xy(x-3y)$ **(c)** $(x+1)(x+2)$
(d) $(x-1)(x-4)$ **(e)** $(x-1)(x+8)$ **(f)** $(x+4)(x+8)$
(g) $(2x+1)(x+2)$ **(h)** $(3x+1)(5x-3)$ **(i)** $(2x-3)(4x-1)$
(j) $(2x^2-1)(x^2+4)$ **(k)** $(x+3)^2$ **(l)** $(x-4)^2$

Revision exercise 2

1 £201.60
2 £4419.69
3 3520, 1760, 1320
4 3.818×10^3
5 **(a)** 1.8×10^9 **(b)** £720 **(c)** 2.2×10^6
6 **(a)** 3×10^{-8} **(b)** 3×10^{-10}
7 **(a)** 1.47×10^8 **(b)** 2.1×10^3 **(c)** 7×10^4
8 **(a)** 20% **(b)** £2.50
9 £92
10 **(a)** 3.62×10^8 **(b)** 5.12×10^8 **(c)** 71%

Revision exercise 3

1 $\sqrt{6}$, 2π

2 $\frac{2}{3}$, 1.6, $\frac{4}{17}$

3 **(a)** Can be written as $\frac{1}{7}$ **(b)** $\sqrt{1}$, $\sqrt{4}$, $\sqrt{9}$

4 **(i)** 3.1, 3.2, etc. **(ii)** $\sqrt{10}$, $\sqrt{11}$, etc.

5 **(a)** **(i)** 91 **(ii)** $\frac{91}{99}$ **(b)** $\frac{99}{101}$ and many more.

6 **(a)** $\sqrt{3} \times \sqrt{12}$, etc. **(b)** $\sqrt{8}$, $\sqrt{2}$, etc.

Revision exercise 4

1 **(a)** 12.5, 12.7
(b) Yes as this lies within the upper and lower bound
2 **(a)** **(i)** 31.894 762 5 **(ii)** 29.442 262 5
(b) 30
3 **(a)** $176.527\,331\,2 < \text{length} < 178.317\,152\,1$ **(b)** 2
4 **(a)** 2.86 **(b)** $66.517\,315\,07\text{ cm}^2$ $66.427\,956\,79\text{ cm}^2$
5 75.3 cm **6** **(i)** 380 cm^2 **(ii)** 460 cm^2
7 **(a)** **(i)** 2.2365 **(ii)** 2.2355 **(b)** **(i)** 3.651 **(ii)** 3.649
(c) 3.159 879 25 **(d)** 1.582 242 66

Revision exercise 5

1 **(a)** $x=6$ **(b)** $x=-3$ **(c)** $x=7\frac{1}{5}$ **(d)** $x=\frac{5}{7}$
(e) $x=2$ **(f)** $x=\frac{9}{11}$ **(g)** $x=\frac{15}{13}$ or $1\frac{2}{3}$ **(h)** $x=-6$

2 **(a)** $p=2$, $q=-1$ **(b)** $x=5$, $y=-2$
(c) $p=3$, $q=-3$ **(d)** $x=4$, $y=-2$

3 $x=0$, or $x=3$

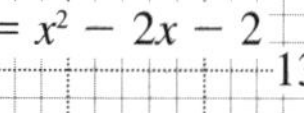

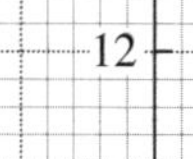
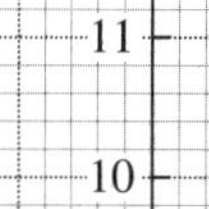
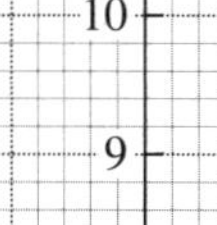
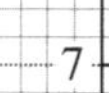

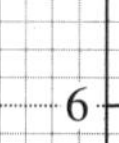
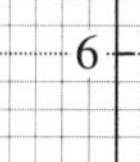
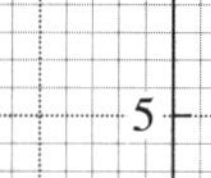
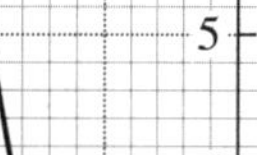
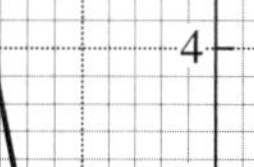
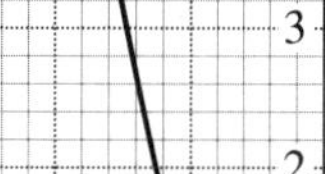

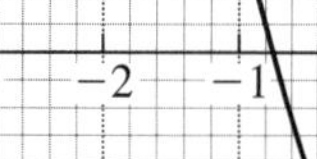
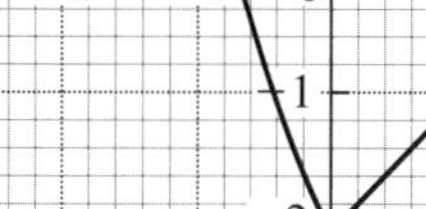
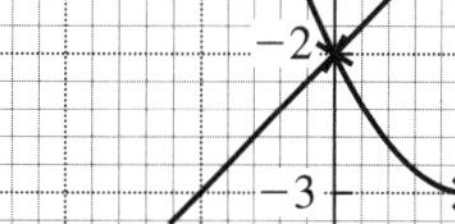

4 (a) (c)

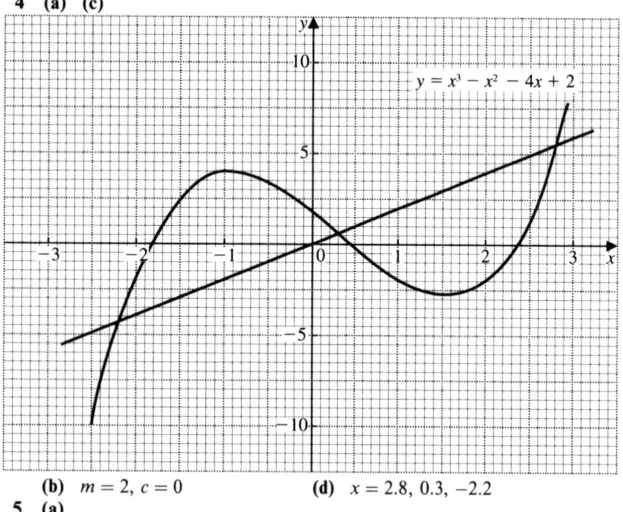

(b) $m = 2$, $c = 0$ **(d)** $x = 2.8, 0.3, -2.2$

5 (a)

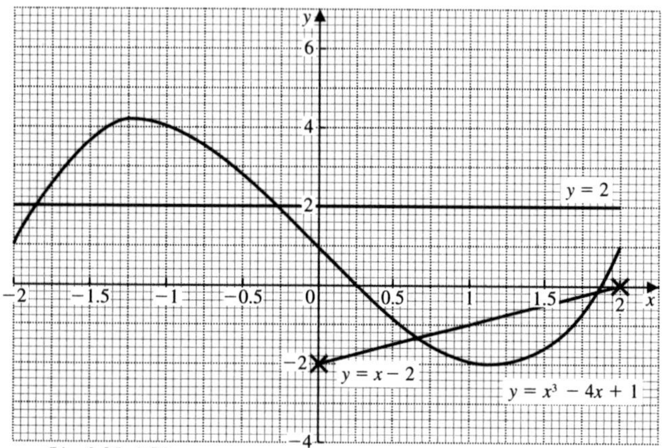

(b) 0.25, 1.75

(c) **(i)** $y = 2$, $x = -0.25$ or -1.75

(ii) $y = x - 2$, $x = 0.65$ or 1.85

6

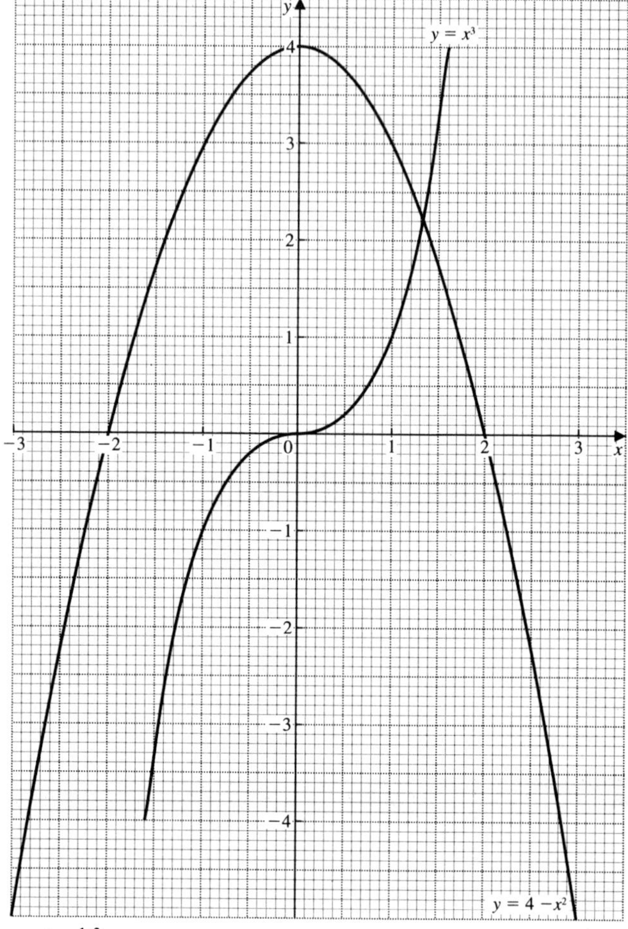

$x = 1.3$

7 3.6

8 2.4

Revision exercise 6

1 **(a)** $\pm\sqrt{5}$ **(b)** 0, 7 **(c)** $-3, -4$
(d) $6, -3$ **(e)** $-6, -4$ **(f)** $8, -2$
(g) $-\frac{1}{2}, 3$ **(h)** $-\frac{2}{5}, 5$ **(i)** $\frac{1}{2}, -\frac{5}{3}$

2 **(a)** $7.41, -0.41$ **(b)** $1.72, -0.39$ **(c)** $3.30, -0.30$
(d) $0.85, -2.35$ **(e)** 2.18, 0.15

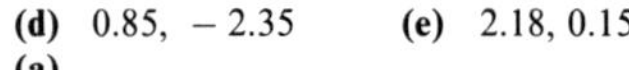
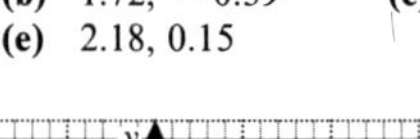

3 **(a)**

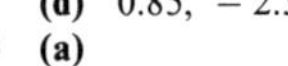

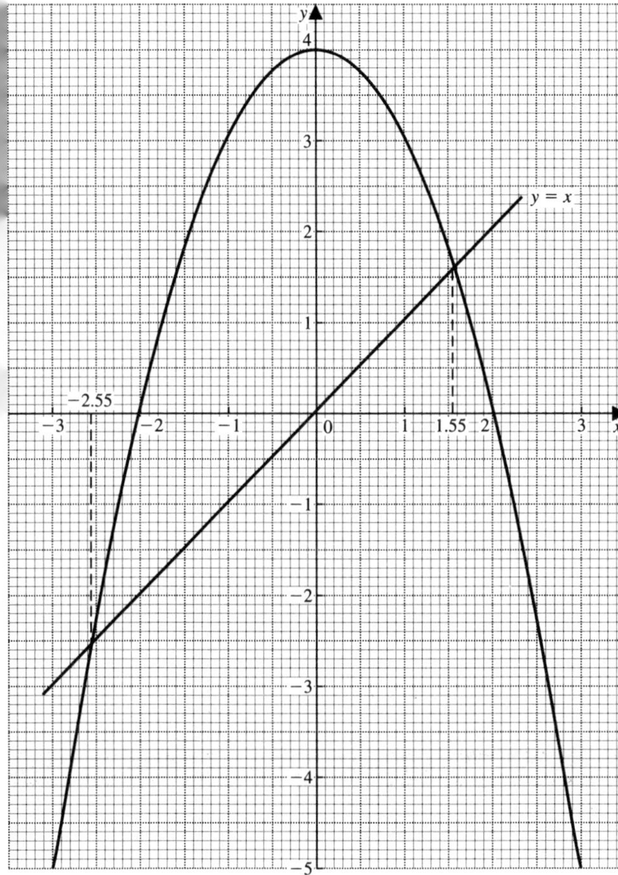

(b) $1.55, -2.55$

4 **(a)** $\frac{20}{x} + \frac{20}{x+2} = 4$ **(c)** 11.1, 0.9

(d) $x = 0.9$ gives a negative speed on homeward journey

5 **(a)** $\frac{12}{x} + \frac{12}{x-2}$ **(b)** **(i)** $\frac{12}{x} + \frac{12}{x-2} = \frac{7}{2}$

(c) $x = 8$

Revision exercise 7

1 **(a)** $x \geqslant 2$ **(b)** $x \leqslant \frac{1}{3}$ **(c)** $x \leqslant 4\frac{1}{2}$ **(d)** $x \leqslant \frac{6}{7}$
(e) $x \geqslant -6$ **(f)** $x \leqslant 3$ **(g)** $x \leqslant \frac{2}{3}$ **(h)** $x < \frac{5}{3}$

2

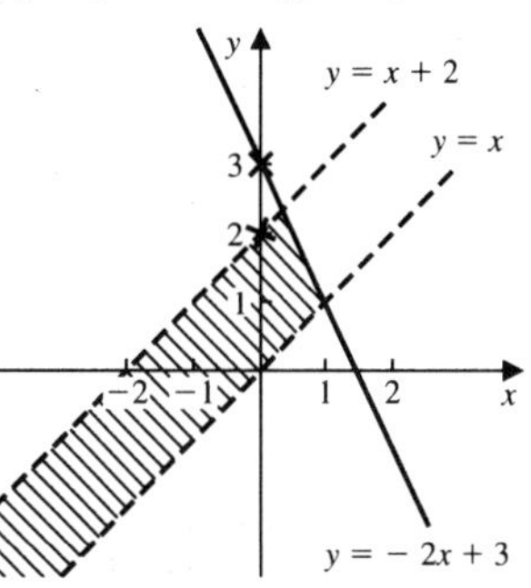

3

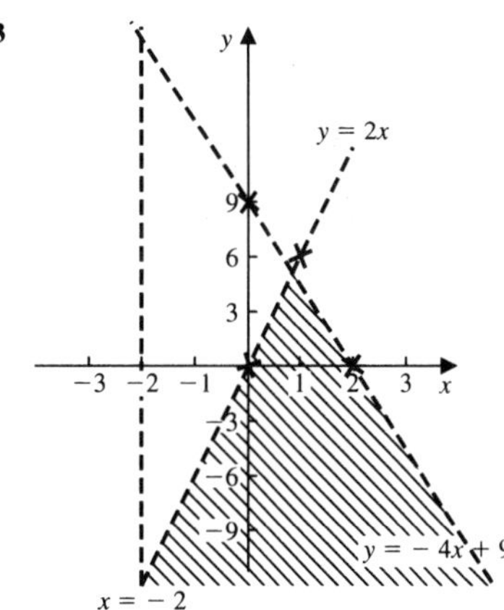

4 **(a)** $-6 < x < 6$ **(b)** $-9 > x > 9$ **(c)** $-\frac{8}{3} < x < \frac{8}{3}$
(d) $-8 \geqslant x \geqslant 6$ **(e)** $8 > x > -2$ **(f)** $-\frac{5}{3} < x < \frac{7}{3}$

5 **(a)** $x \leqslant 1\frac{3}{4}$ **(b)**

x = 3 y = 4x + 6 y = 13

Revision exercise 8

1 **(a)** $c = 1.4a$
(b) **(i)** 70p **(ii)** 98p **(iii)** £1.89 **(iv)** £3.08
(c) 125 ml

2 **(a)** $d = kt^2$ **(b)** $k = 5$ **(c)** 80 m **(d)** 10 s

3 **(a)** $f = \frac{k}{w}$ **(b)** $k = 3200$ **(c)** **(i)** 640 **(ii)** 16 000
(d) 0.64

4 3.83 litres

5 **(a)** $a = kb^3$ **(b)** $k = 2$ **(c)** 432 **(d)** 7

6 **(a)** 500 **(b)** ± 6

7 180 feet

8 **(a)** $t = \frac{k}{V}$ **(b)** 40 000

Revision exercise 9

1 **(a)** −3 **(b)** 2
(c) 17 **(d)** 122

2 **(a)**

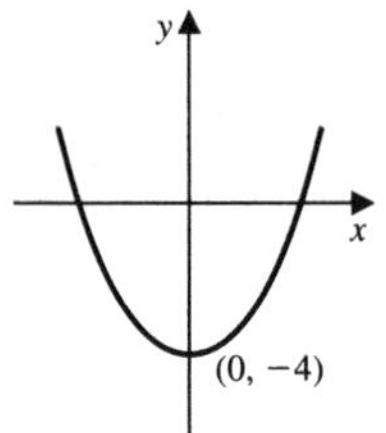

(b)

(4, 0)

3 **(a)** **(i)** Same graph translated −1 vertically along y-axis.
(ii) Same graph translated −1 horizontally along x-axis.

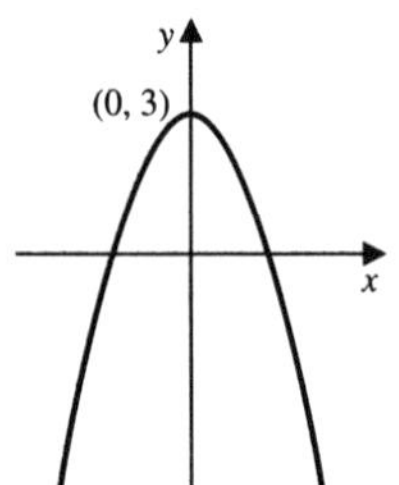

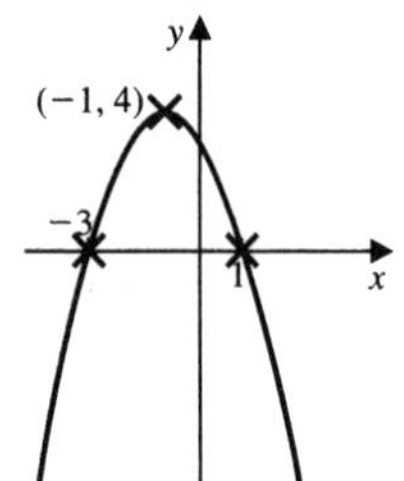

(b)

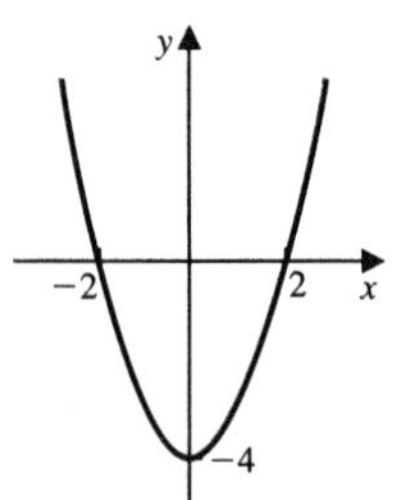

4 **(a)**

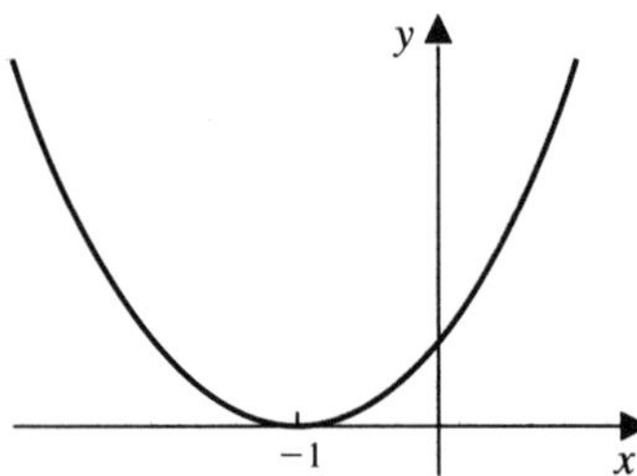

(b) $-\frac{1}{2}$ **(c)** 2, −4

5

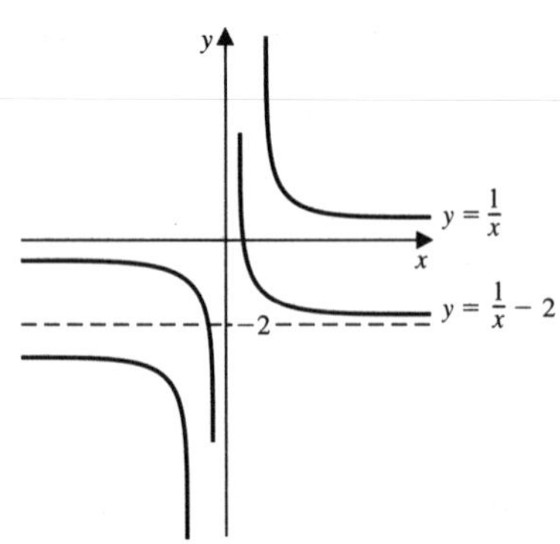

6

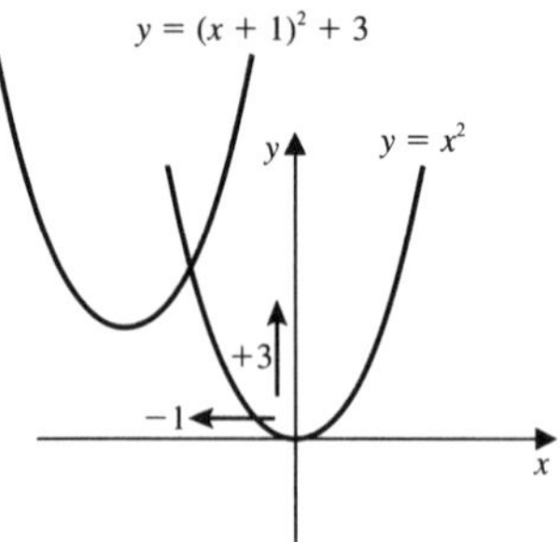

7 **(a)** **(b)**

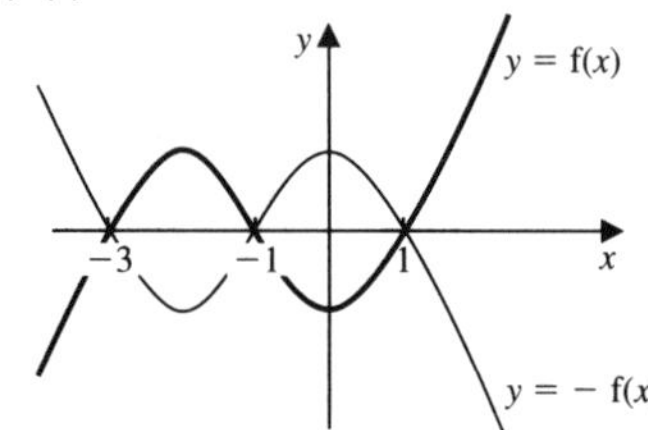

(c) A reflection in the x-axis

8

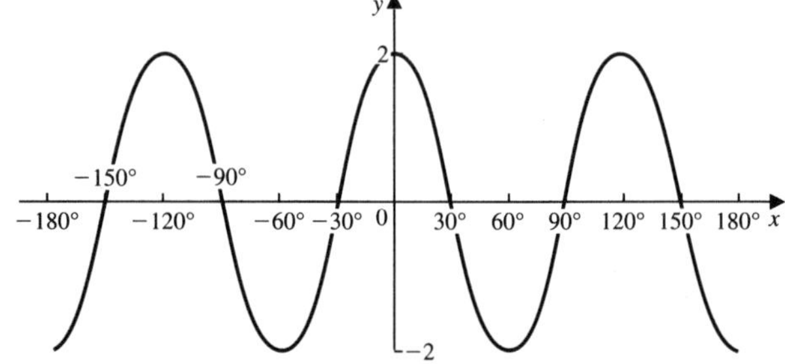

Revision exercise 10

1 **(a)**

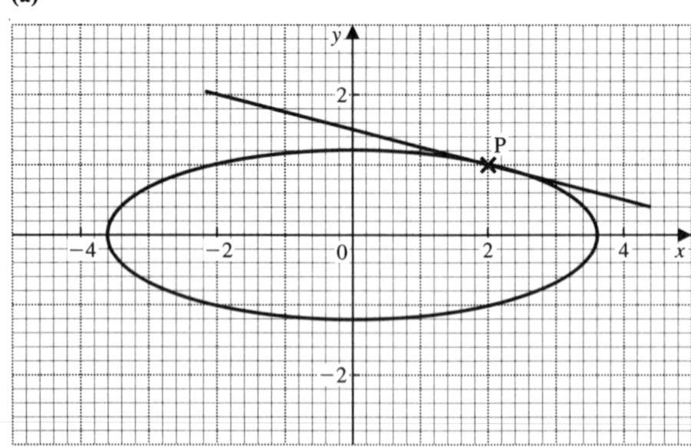

(b) −0.3

2 2

3 **(a)** 15.3 **(b)** The rate of change of height with respect to age.

4 **(a)** 1011 **(b)** 1005, 1008 **(c)** 1001, 1004

5 **(a)** $0.4\,\text{m s}^{-2}$ **(b)** 1185 m

6 **(a)** $-1.2\,\text{m s}^{-2}$ **(b)** Deceleration of $1.2\,\text{m s}^{-2}$ **(c)** 557 m

Revision exercise 11

1 $p = 3,\ q = 4,\ y = 3(4)^x$

2 $p = 2^{\frac{1}{3}},\ q = 2^{\frac{2}{3}},\ y = 2^{\frac{2}{3}}(2^{\frac{1}{3}})^x = 2^{\frac{x+2}{3}}$

3 **(a)**

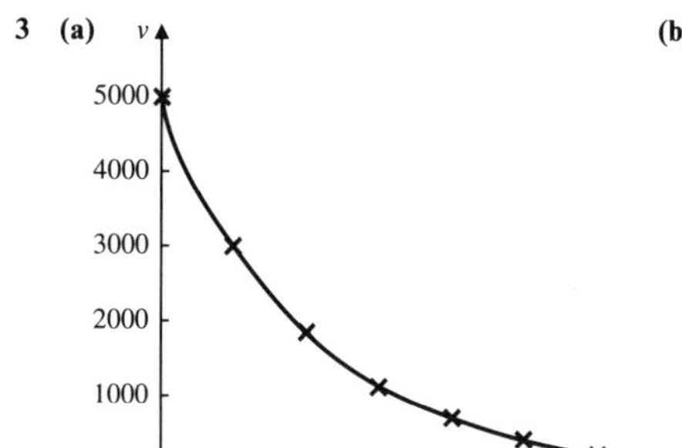

(b) $p = 5000,\ q = 0.6$

4 **(a)** **(b)** $a = 2.5,\ b = 0.5$

5 **(a)** **(b)** $a = 6.4,\ b = 39$

6 **(a)** **(b)** $a = 2.5,\ b = 1.2$

7 **(a)** **(i)** t^2 values: 0.3136, 0.5041, 0.9409, 1.1236, 1.2544, 1.5625

(ii) The values all lie on a straight line passing through the origin.

(b) 16.

Revision exercise 12

1 **(a)** 40.97 cm **(b)** 50.91 cm^2 **(c)** 19.5°
2 **(a)** 300 km **(b)** 337° **(c)** 46.2 km
3 **(a)** 16.16 cm **(b)** 16.91 cm **(c)** 17.2°
4 13.4 m
5 **(a)** 8 cm **(b)** 28.3 cm **(c)** 28.1° **(d)** 15.8°
6 **(a)** 16.97 cm **(b)** 8.485 cm **(c)** 70.2°
7 **(a)** 77.3° **(b)** 9 cm **(c)** 15 cm **(d)** 73.3°
8 24.57 cm
9 Examples include:
(i) 3, 4, 5 **(ii)** 3, $\sqrt{3}$, $\sqrt{6}$ **(iii)** $\sqrt{2}$, 1, 1 **(iv)** 2, 1, $\sqrt{3}$

Revision exercise 13

1 16 m **2** **(a)** 5.25 cm **(b)** *ECD*, *FCE*
3 **(a)** $P'(0, -1)$, $Q'(-1, -1)$, $R'(-1, -3)$
4 **(a)** $C\hat{A}B = Y\hat{X}B$; $\hat{B}$ common. So corresponding angles are equal.
(b) $6\frac{6}{7}$ **(c)** $\frac{49}{16}$
5 S, S'' are congruent. Overall scale factor is -1.
6 $4\frac{8}{13}$ cm

Revision exercise 14

1 **(a)** $x = 8.08$ cm, area $= 32.1\ cm^2$
(b) $x = 12.4$ cm, area $= 25.4\ cm^2$
2 283°
3 5
4 **(a)** 43.3 km **(b)** 7.2 km/h and 10.87 km/h
5 33.6 m
6 36.9°
7 **(a)** 23.35 m **(b)** 62.7°
8 **(a)** 52.34° and 127.66° **(b)** 9.52 cm and 18.04 cm
9 **(a)** 203.56 km **(b)** 047° **(c)** 30.71 km
10 17.3°

Revision exercise 15

1 15°, 75°
2
3 71.56° only
4 60°, 300°, −60°, −300°
5 30°, −30°, 150°, −150°
6

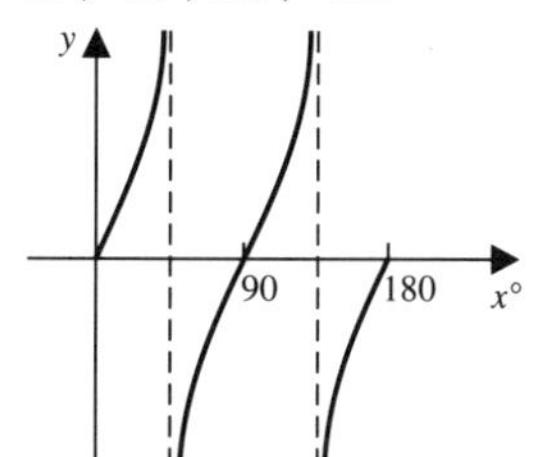

7 **(a)** max = 5 at $x = 90°$ **(b)** min = −5 at $x = 270°$
8 53.13° and −53.13°

Revision exercise 16

1 **(a)** Translation, 6 units to the right
(b) Translation, 6 units to the left

2 **(a)** **(i)**

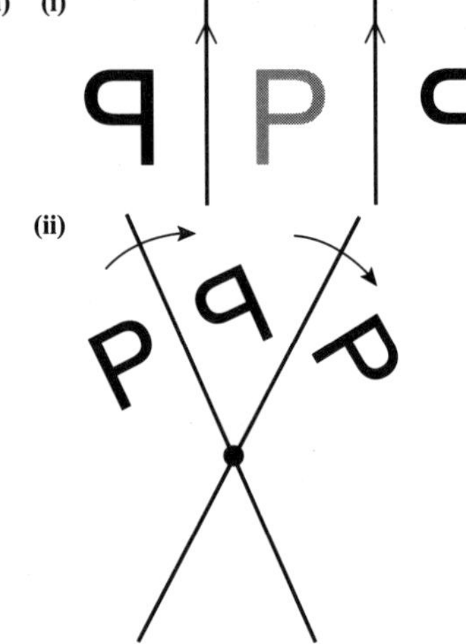

(ii)

(b) Rotation about the point of intersection of the two lines through an angle twice the size of the angle between the two lines.

3 **(a)** Rotation 180° about $\left(-\frac{1}{2}, \frac{1}{2}\right)$

(b) Rotation 180° about $\left(-\frac{1}{2}, \frac{1}{2}\right)$

4 Rotation about (0, 0) through 90° anticlockwise.

5 **(a)** $A''(6, 6)$ $B''(12, 6)$ $C''(6, 18)$

(b) Enlargement, scale factor 6, centre (0, 0).

6 **(a)** Enlargement centre X, scale factor k^2.

(b) Enlargement centre X, scale factor $\frac{1}{k^2}$.

Revision exercise 17

1 15 cm²

2 **(a)** 1230 m **(b)** 31 400

3 1005.3 cm³

4 **(a)** 20 cm **(b)** 21.93 cm

5 **(a)** 5.20 cm **(b)** 589.5 cm³

6 869.3 cm³

7 27.95 cm

8 **(a)** 301.6 cm³ **(b)** 271 g

9 **(a)** 330.9 m **(b)** 6545 m²

10 **(a)** 169.65 cm³ **(b)** 2.95 cm **(c)** 6.7%

Revision exercise 18

1 **(a)**

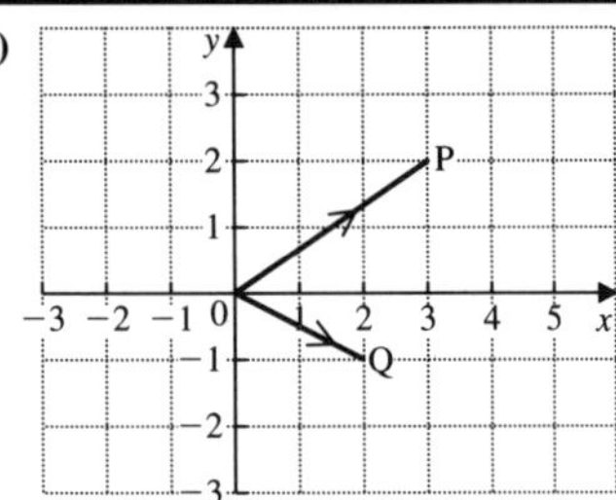

(b) $\begin{pmatrix} 5 \\ 1 \end{pmatrix}$

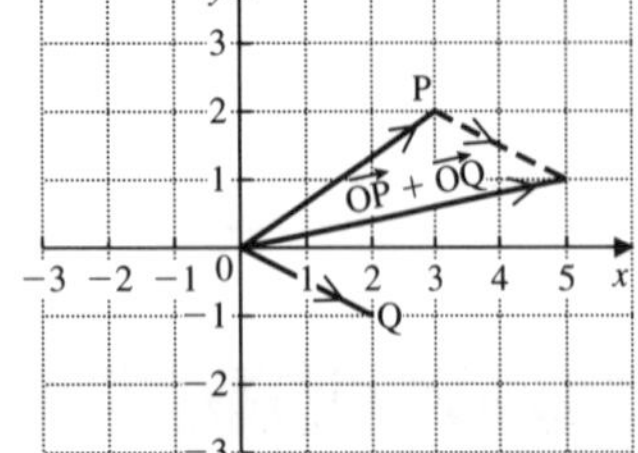

(c) $\begin{pmatrix} 1 \\ 3 \end{pmatrix}$

2 $\mathbf{a} + 4\mathbf{b} = \begin{pmatrix} 10 \\ 12 \end{pmatrix} = 2\mathbf{c}$

3 $\begin{pmatrix} 4 \\ 6 \end{pmatrix}$

4 **(a)** $\mathbf{a} + \mathbf{b}$ **(b)** $\overrightarrow{PQ} = \frac{2}{5}\mathbf{b} - \frac{4}{15}\mathbf{a}$

(c) No, it is not a multiple of **b**

5 **(a)** $2\mathbf{a}$ **(b)** $3\mathbf{a} + \mathbf{b}$ **(c)** $2\mathbf{a} + 2\mathbf{b}$

(d) $\frac{3\mathbf{a}}{2} + \frac{\mathbf{b}}{2}$

6 **(a)** $\mathbf{y} - \mathbf{x}$

(b) $\overrightarrow{QT} = 2\mathbf{y} - 2\mathbf{x}$ so $\overrightarrow{QT} \parallel \overrightarrow{PQ}$ and point Q is common, so PQT is a straight line.

7 **(a)** **(i)** $\mathbf{b} - \mathbf{a}$ **(ii)** $2\mathbf{a}$ **(iii)** $2\mathbf{b} - 2\mathbf{a}$

(b) They are parallel.

Revision exercise 19

1 17°

2 $x = 62°$, $y = 118°$

3 **(a)** $x = 47°$ **(b)** $y = 48°$

4 **(a)** 48° (alternate segment)

(b) 70° (cyclic quadrilateral, $B\hat{C}D = 110°$)

(c) 132° (angles in triangle)

(d) 24° (angles in triangle with $B\hat{D}A = 62°$ and $B\hat{D}X = B\hat{X}D$, isosceles triangle)

5 $B\hat{E}D = B\hat{D}E$ ($BE = BD$)

So $B\hat{D}E = \frac{180 - x}{2} = 90 - \frac{x}{2}$

Similarly $C\hat{D}F = 90 - \frac{y}{2}$

$B\hat{D}E + C\hat{D}F + E\hat{D}F = 180°$

So $E\hat{D}F = \frac{x}{2} + \frac{y}{2}$ or $\frac{x + y}{2}$ or $\frac{1}{2}(x + y)$

6 **(a)** $x°$ (alternate segment)

(b) $180° - x°$ ($B\hat{D}C = x°$, isosceles triangle and $A\hat{D}B + x = 180°$, straight line)

7 **(a)** Angles at $\hat{P}$ and $\hat{Q} = 90°$, so $\hat{P} + \hat{Q} = 180°$. Hence $OPTQ$ is cyclic.

(b) 14.2 cm

Revision exercise 20

1 **(a)** 19 **(b)** 19

2 Select, at random, a number between 1 and 20 – call it n. Sample nth, $(n + 20)$th, $(n + 40)$th, etc.

3 **(a)** 498 **(b)** 1224 **(c)** 1434

Revision exercise 21

1 30.9 g

2 **(a)** $20 < t \leqslant 30$ **(b)** 18 min

(c)

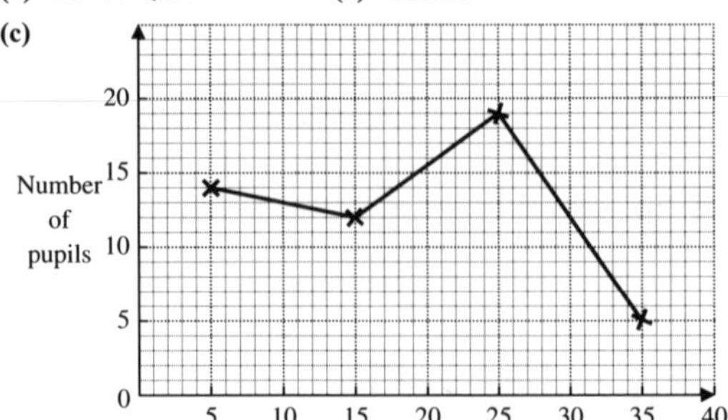

3 285 g

4 1.2125 hours.

Revision exercise 22

1 (a)

	< 10	< 20	< 30	< 40	<50	< 60
Cf	20	38	44	48	50	52

(b)

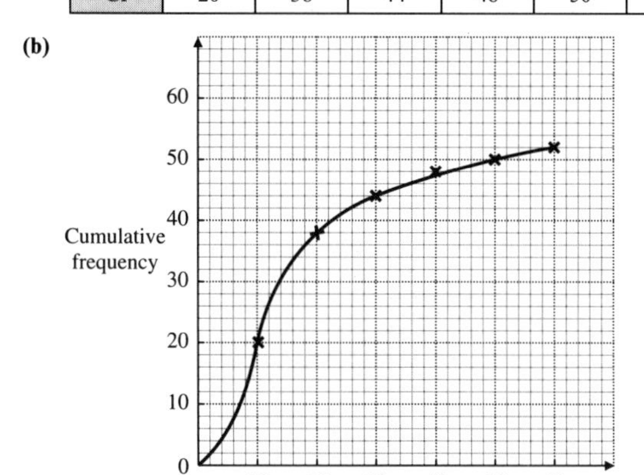

(c) Approx. 13 mm **(d)** Approx. 13.5 mm **(e)** 30.

2 (a)

	< 1.5	< 2.0	< 2.5	< 3.0	< 3.5	< 4.0	< 4.5	< 5.0
Cf	4	13	24	45	71	89	98	100

(b)

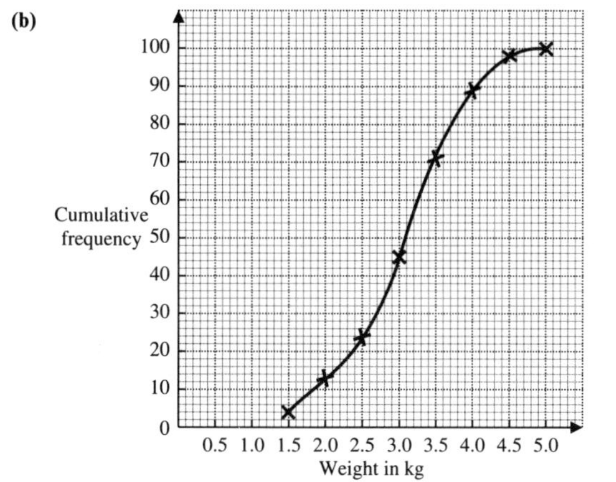

(c) Approx. 3.1 kg **(d)** Approx 1 kg (e) Approx. 60%

3 (a) Cumulative frequencies are 2, 3, 6, 14, 25, 29, 31

(b)

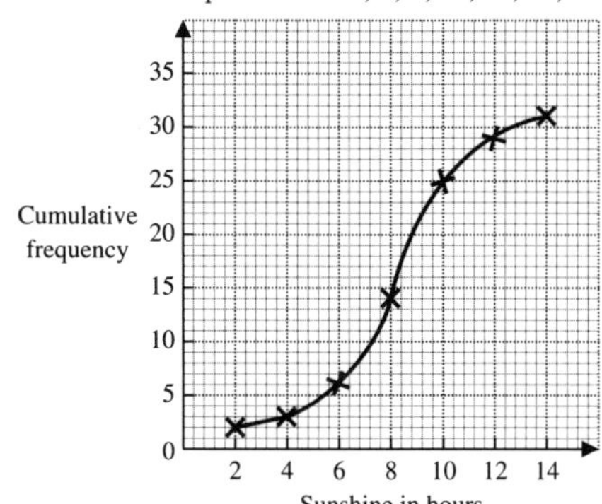

(c) Approx. 8.2 hours
(d) Approx. 3 hours
(e) Ashwell median > Downtown median and the two interquartile ranges are about the same.
So Ashwell generally had more sunshine.

4 (a) Cumulative frequencies are 10, 30, 65, 90, 98, 100.
(b)

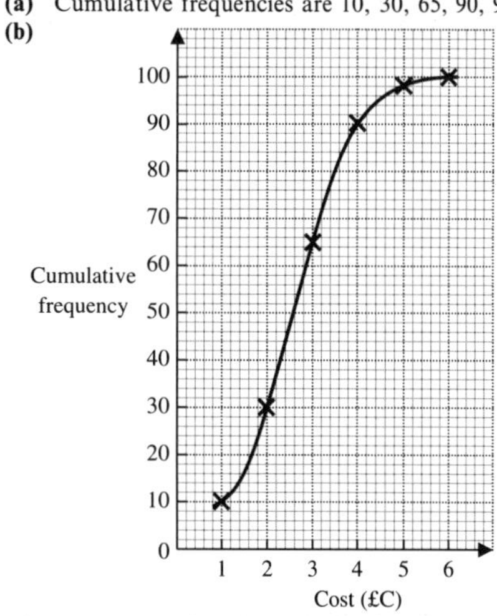

(c) **(i)** £2.50 approx **(ii)** £1.80 approx
(iii) £3.30 approx **(iv)** 16% approx

Revision exercise 23

1 Frequency column is: 32, 20, 18, 4.
2 (a) 210.2g and 10.14 g
(b) The means are similar with Brand slightly lower, but the spread for Brand coffee B much greater so the jars could contain much more or much less than Nicer jars.
3 (a) 2.5 **(b)** 12.5
5 (a) 5
(b)

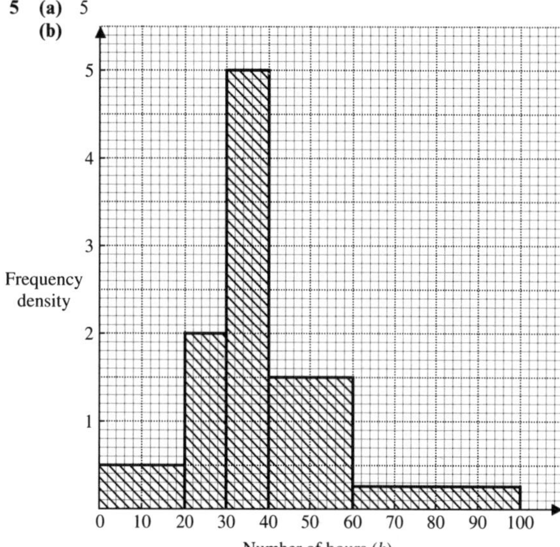

6 1.374 (to 3 d.p.)
7

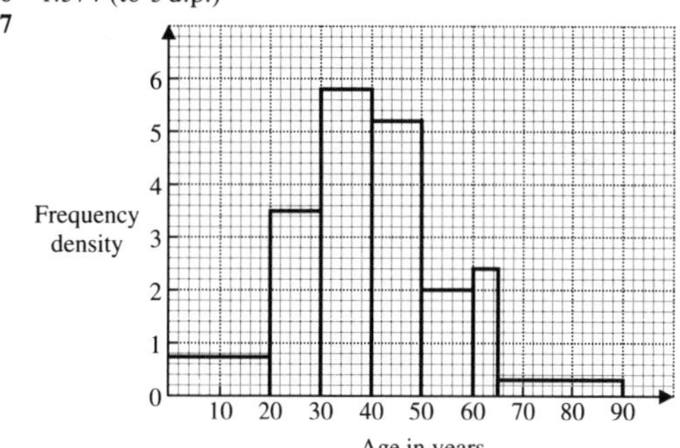

Revision exercise 24

1 **(a)** 1600 **(b)** 0.4 **(c)** 0.1 **(d)** 0.98

2 **(a)**

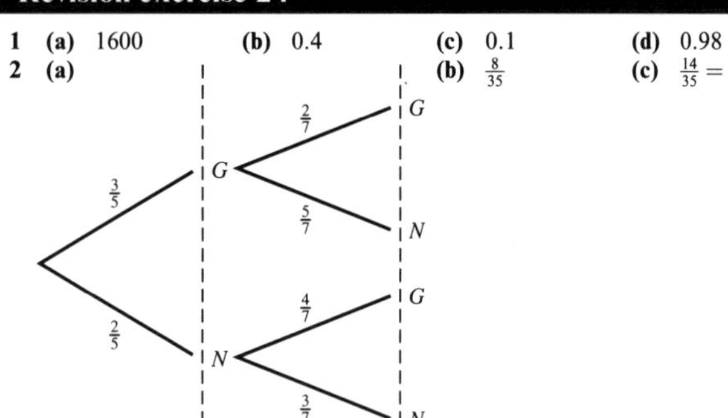

(b) $\frac{8}{35}$ **(c)** $\frac{14}{35} = \frac{2}{5}$

3 $\frac{31}{72}$ **4** $\frac{23}{60}$

5 **(a)** $\frac{4}{5}$ **(b)** $\frac{15}{19}$ **(c)** **(i)** $\frac{12}{19}$ **(ii)** $\frac{32}{95}$

6 $\frac{3}{44}$

Examination practice paper Answers

1 **(a)** £54.40 **(b)** £35

2 **(a)** $27 - 12 < 30$, $64 - 16 > 30$ **(b)** 3.5

3 **(a)** 8 **(b)** $\frac{1}{3}$

4 $x = 3$, $y = -1$

5 36°

6 **(a)** 1696.46 cm^3 **(b)** 11.93 cm

7 **(a)** $2xy(x^2 + 3y^2)$ **(b)** $x = -\frac{7}{5}$

(c) **(i)** $(x - 7)(x + 4)$ **(ii)** $x = 7$ **or** -4

8 **(a)**

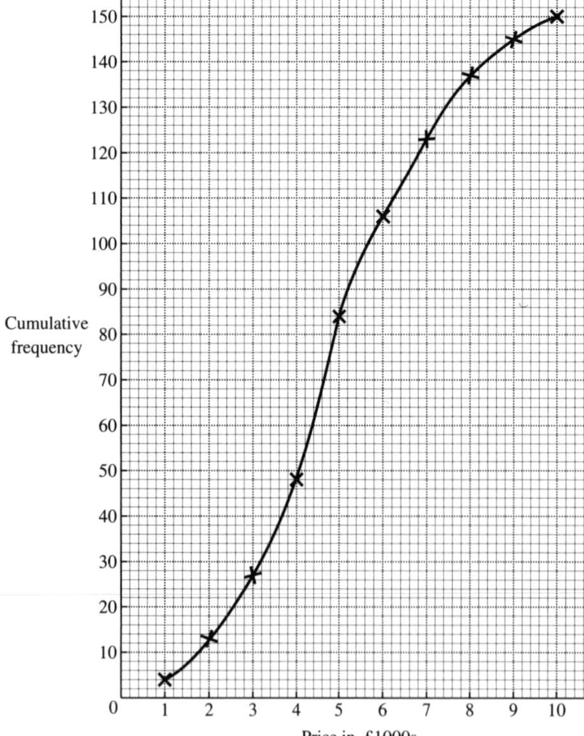

(b) **(i)** approx £4750 **(ii)** approx £2750

9 **(a)** **(i)** 16.55 cm **(ii)** 8 cm

(b) 41.2° **(c)** 140 cm^3

10 **(a)** 3.75×10^4 **(b)** 1.65×10^5

11 **(a)**

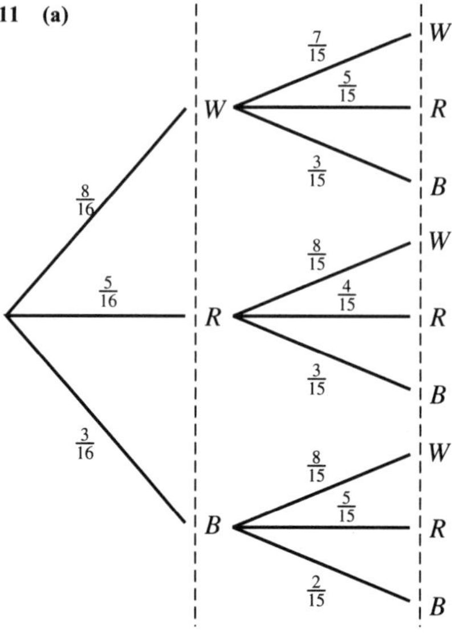

(b) **(i)** $\frac{1}{12}$ **(ii)** $\frac{41}{120}$

12 147.5 km

13 $\frac{4}{3}\pi r^3 = 2r$, so $r^2 = \dfrac{3}{2\pi}$, $r = \sqrt{\dfrac{3}{2\pi}}$

14 **(a)** n is not a perfect square

(b) $p + \sqrt{n}$ and $q + \sqrt{n}$ are irrational if p and q are rational and different and n is not a perfect square.
Then $(p + \sqrt{n}) - (q + \sqrt{n}) = p - q$, which will be rational.

15 $\sqrt{\dfrac{x^2 + x^2 + (2 - x)^2 + (3 - x)^2 + (4x - 5)^2}{5}}$

16 **(a)** $ax + b = mx + c$, $(a - m)x = c - b$

(b) Parallel lines, no point of intersection. They are concurrent.

17 **(i)** $\mathbf{a} + \mathbf{b}$ **(ii)** $2\mathbf{b} - \mathbf{a}$ **(iii)** $3\mathbf{b} - \mathbf{a}$

18 **(i)** $(2x - y)(2x + y)$ **(ii)** $x = 3$, $y = 1$

19 4

20 (3, 2)

Heinemann Educational Publishers
Halley Court, Jordan Hill, Oxford, OX2 8EJ
a division of Reed Educational & Professional Publishing Ltd

OXFORD MELBOURNE AUCKLAND
JOHANNESBURG BLANTYRE GABORONE
IBADAN PORTSMOUTH (NH) USA CHICAGO

First published 1997

00 01 10 9 8

ISBN 0 435 53220 0

Original design by Wendi Watson

Typeset and illustrated by Tech-Set Limited, Gateshead, Tyne & Wear

Printed in Great Britain by The Bath Press, Bath

Acknowledgements

The publisher's and author's thanks are due to London Examinations for permission to reproduce questions from past examination papers. These are marked with an [L]. The answers have been provided by the authors and are not the responsibility of the Examining Council.